HOW TO KNOW
THE
LAND BIRDS

Pictured-Keys for determining all of the Land Birds
of the entire United States and Southern Canada,
with maps showing their geographic distribution, and
other helpful features.

by

H. E. JAQUES
Professor of Biology
Iowa Wesleyan College

FIRST EDITION

WM. C. BROWN COMPANY
Publishers
DUBUQUE, IOWA

*Some one has suggested that we show the pronounci-
ation of our name. It doesn't make much difference, for
even our friends have several forms for it, — but here
it is:*

Jaques — Jā'-kwis

Copyright 1947
by H. E. Jaques

THE PICTURED-KEY NATURE SERIES

"How to Know the Insects," Jaques, 1947

"Living Things—How to Know Them," Jaques, 1946

"How to Know the Trees," Jaques, 1946

"Plant Families—How to Know Them," Jaques, 1948

"How to Know the Spring Flowers," Cuthbert, 1943, 1949

"How to Know the Mosses and Liverworts," Conard, 1944, 1956

"How to Know the Land Birds," Jaques, 1947

"How to Know the Fall Flowers," Cuthbert, 1948

"How to Know the Immature Insects," Chu, 1949

"How to Know the Protozoa," Jahn, 1949

"How to Know the Mammals," Booth, 1949

"How to Know the Beetles," Jaques, 1951

"How to Know the Spiders," Kaston, 1952

"How to Know the Grasses," Pohl, 1953

"How to Know the Fresh-Water Algae," Prescott, 1954

"How to Know the Western Trees," Baerg, 1955

"How to Know the Seaweeds," Dawson, 1956

"How to Know the Freshwater Fishes," Eddy, 1957

In Both Spiral and Cloth Binding
Other Subjects in Preparation

Printed in U.S.A.

CONTENTS

1133475

CONTENTS

INTRODUCTION

he Pictured-Key Nature Books specialize in identification. Every effort is being made to keep them so simple and understandable, that any one can quickly determine the correct name of a bird, tree or insect family, etc.

The observation and study of birds appeals to all ages. It is a delightful pastime for casual moments or may be pursued intensely with genuine pleasure and profit.

Almost every species of Land Bird known to live within the United States and Southern Canada is herein pictured, keyed and described. The characters most apparent in the field have been used in the keys while other essential facts about the bird in question, are recorded in the descriptions. Truthfulness has been the constant aim in making the pictures. Determining characters have often been given some special emphasis. It will be noted that each bird picture bears the A. O. U. check number for that bird.

Many of our birds take on somewhat different appearances in separate parts of our great area. Bird students have used these minor differences as characters in naming subspecies. These subspecies with their check numbers, are listed throughout the book, and their differences given.

With almost every bird is a map showing its geographic distribution. Usually the map reveals the area taken by each subspecies, which is labeled with the catalog number or the letter part of the number. It should be understood that these distribution areas are only approximate. One should not be greatly surprised if he finds some birds outside of its mapped region.

The drawings have been made by Mrs. Martha W. Cutkomp. Many others have helped with the book. We wish to express our appreciation to all these.

The book has been produced in response to the repeated call for a bird book written in the style of the Pictured-Key Nature Series. Work is already under way for a second volume similarly treating the Water Birds. It is hoped it can be completed without too much delay. The two volumes will then include all the living birds of the entire United States and Southern Canada. A Field Notebook for conviently recording bird observations and data is also now available.

Mt. Pleasant, Iowa
December, 1946

1

SOME EXPLANATIONS ABOUT BIRDS

 ext to a few household pets some of our very earliest interests in living things are with birds. They are noticed by every one. Their observation and study takes one to the Out-of-doors and for health giving interest ranks high as a hobby. Birds touch our living in so many ways, economically and otherwise, that a knowledge of them is a very definite cultural asset.

Scientists in their world-wide search have found, named and described more than 900,000 different species of animals. Only 60,000 of these are vertebrates. Five well known classes *Fish, Amphibians, Reptiles, Birds* and *Mammals* include almost all of these possessors of backbones. Twenty-five thousand are birds.

Now mammals have hair, fish and reptiles usually have scales while the frogs and their kin are naked skinned. Birds differ from all other animals in being covered with *feathers*.

Their ability with long sustained flight takes them to all parts of the world. Almost anywhere that man may go he has the opportunity to study birds.

Pre-historic Birds

Birds do not lend themselves readily to fossil making. Our knowledge of early birds is very much limited. The oldest known fossil specimen (Fig. 1) was found in Europe and dates back perhaps 125,000,000 years or more. About the size of a crow, it had several reptilian characters but its covering of feathers definitely made it a bird. Fossil birds of a considerably later period but still very old ones are known from Western Kansas.

Figure 1. An artist's restoration of Archaeopteryx.

Size of Birds

Mythology speaks of some very large birds. The "Elephant Birds" which became extinct on the island of Madagascar only two or three centuries ago are the world's largest of which we have definite knowledge. These flightless, heavy-legged birds have left their records in bones and eggs. Some of these eggs buried in the sand measure over 13 inches in length and have a capacity of more than two gallons.

In contrast the African Ostrich, our largest living bird, weighs over three hundred pounds and stands eight feet high. At the other extreme are some of the Hummingbirds, tiny little fellows 3 inches or less in length but with the ultimate in perfection of form and coloring yet so dainty as to make but scant impression on the scales. The relative sizes of these eggs are shown here (Fig. 2).

About Feathers

Figure 2. Comparative sizes of eggs. A, Sparrow; B, Hummingbird; C, Crow; D, Elephant Bird (extinct); E, Ostrich; F, Robin.

Feathers are highly intricate outgrowths of the skin. They function in giving protection, insulation and resistance to air currents. To be efficient they must combine the maximum of strength, waterproofing and insulation qualities with the minimum of weight. Outwardly they seem to arise uniformly from all parts of the bird. A little observance when one "picks" a chicken or other bird reveals large bare areas supporting no feathers. Next to the skin are *downy feathers* for warmth, overgrown by *contour feathers* which form much of the surface and give pattern and color to the bird. The largest and best formed contour feathers are usually those of tail and wings (often called flight feathers). Some contour feathers are highly specialized for ornamental purposes.

Practically every conceivable color, shade and tint may be found in feathers. Often this coloration is due to actual pigments in the feathers; in other instances the feather surface refracts the light in a way to produce color effect different from that of the actual pigment possessed by the feather. Greens always, blues usually, and yellow sometimes belong here. Then feathers often display iridescence, their apparent color chang-

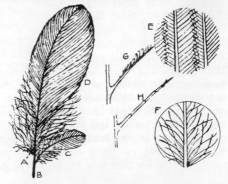

Figure 3. Parts of a Feather; A, rhachis; B, calamus; C, after-shaft; D, vane; E, two barbs with overlapping barbules; F, barb of down feathers; G, barbule with barbicels; H, plain barb.

ing with the angle at which they are viewed. The hummingbirds are excellent examples of iridescent coloring.

3

Birds occasionally lose their pigment and are *albinos*. Albinism may effect the entire bird or only some areas. Robins are frequently seen with large white spots and are sometimes wholly white. One we observed on several occasions recently had the head, primaries and tail nearly black, a narrow red stripe about a quarter of an inch wide down the middle of the breast with all other parts white (Fig. 4).

The irregularity in pigment may run in the other direction causing occasional black or very dark forms. These are said to be *melanos*. Some birds like the Screech Owl have two color phases often in the same brood. That is *dichromatism*. The male bird of a species is frequently marked and colored more brilliantly than his mate. That is *sex-dimorphism*.

Figure 4

Since feathers wear out Nature has provided for their replacement. All birds lose their feathers in the fall (gradually of course) and grow a whole new set *(molt)*. Some birds also have a more or less complete molt in the spring. These two molts may result in birds having entirely different markings during winter than they do in summer with still other color patterns while a molt is in process.

Then again climatic conditions have seemed to result in regional variations of darker or lighter colored birds or larger and smaller forms. Bird specialists have been quick to name these as subspecies. Twenty-six different subspecies of the Song Sparrow and 16 subspecies of the Fox Sparrow are thus recognized.

Good and Bad Birds

Man judges the value of the living things around him by the way they touch his health of his finances. Birds are neither wholly good or entirely bad. They eat immense quantities of insects which would otherwise destroy our crops and we count them highly beneficial but some of these same species may strip a cherry tree of its fruit and someone then is for promptly killing them. Some owls and hawks occasionally feed on birds or domestic poultry but at the same time more than repay that loss by keeping small rodents in check.

It takes a lot of careful observing to decide accurately whether a bird is more harmful than good. Federal and state agencies and other research organization which study these matters thoroughly are usually in much better position to pass on the value of a species than are private individuals.

Migration

Figure 5

Some birds spend practically their whole life in a rather closely restricted region while other species alternately live at summer and winter homes sometimes thousands of miles apart. Several factors are involved in migration but food is likely the most important one. The reader's region has some birds seen only during the breeding season of summer; others that visit his area only in the winter; some that may be observed when their spring and fall migration is on and still other permanent residents that remain the entire year. Then of course a region may occasionally get an *accidental visitant* which has been blown off its course or brought in by some other artificial means.

Bird Names

Beginners in studying plants and animals seem sometimes over-awed by scientific names. They are not nearly so difficult as some would believe and have been genuine lifesavers in bringing stability to the study of plants and animals. The American Ornithologists' Union has done such a grand job in standardizing one common (or English) name for each bird that the use of scientific names seems a bit less necessary with birds than with any other class of living things. These A. O. U. common names have been closely followed in this book. Bird students will do well to hold themselves to their use in speaking of birds.

While these common names apply only where the English language is spoken, scientific names are the same the world over. All birds belong to the Class *Aves* just as all Mammals and all Fishes are in classes by themselves. Classes are divided into Orders. It takes twelve of the 26 orders of living birds, to account for the Land Birds of our region. Orders are divided into *families*. Order 26, the *Passeriformes* is largest of all in numbers of species. Of its 27 families 24 are represented in the region covered by this book. Families are broken up into *genera* and genera into *species*. The name of the genus (which is always capitalized) followed by the species name (beginning with a small letter) constitutes the *scientific name*. Scientific names are printed in Italic type or underscored. Thus all crows belong to the genus *Corvus*. The species name of our common crow is *brachyrhynchos* making its scientific name *Corvus brachyrhynchos*. The abbreviated or full name of the scientist devising a scientific name (known as the *author* or *authority*) frequently follows a scientific name. This name is not italicized. When subspecies are recognized the species name is repeated as the subspecies name of the "type subspecies".

Thus the Eastern Crow is *Corvus brachyrhynchos brachyrhynchos* Brehm. and the Southern Crow, *Corvus brachyrhynchos paulus* Howell. Where several birds of the same genus and species are mentioned in series, it is often customary to give the full scientific name of only the first member of the series and for the others to use only the initials of the repeated words. The Western Crow could then be written *C. b. hesperis* Ridgway.

The question will likely come to many beginners, "Why does the book not show the type subspecies for some of the birds it contains? The answer is this — Many of our birds as well as visiting our territory, range through many of the countries south of us. The type subspecies of some of these birds could be readily found in Mexico or farther south but do not reach our border. Such information as well as quantities of interesting facts about all our birds have been purposely omitted to keep the size and price of the book such that it can be of the greatest service.

A. O. U. Check Numbers

Another notable contribution of the A. O. U. is its series of catalog or check numbers which have been kept unchanged from the beginning. Since the ideas of taxonomists change as they give further study to a situation the A. O. U. numbers no longer take their natural sequence when the birds are listed according to their relations to each other. Never-the-less the numbers are a great convenience in designating a species just as positively as either its common or scientific name. These A. O. U. check list numbers appear both within the text and on the pictures and maps in this book.

Bird Eggs and Young

All birds are *oviparous*. That is they reproduce by laying eggs which must be incubated and from which, after a period of growth as an *embryo*, the young bird hatches in a more or less helpless state. Some birds lay relatively large eggs which require a longer incubation period but from which *precocial* young emerge, protected with fluffy feathers, and ready to run and pick up their own food almost immediately. These active little fellows soon leave the nest and follow the mother around in search of food and drink which she shows them how to find and take. (Fig. 6). They collect under the mother for protection and warmth at night, when tired or during storms, but are at other times living an active life. Examples of such precocial birds are Domestic

Figure 6

Chickens, Ducks, Quails, Terns, etc. Aquatic precocials like ducks and terns can swim as soon as they are out of the shell, without even being shown how. Several weeks or even months elapse before the flight feathers mature and the ability to fly is acquired. The young of Pigeons, Owls, or Robins for example, when first hatched are largely naked. They have but strength enough to hold the rather large head up for the few moments required for the parent bird to poke some food into the widely opened mouth. They remain in the nest for a considerable period of time and consume immense quantities of food before being able to walk or fly. (Fig. 7). These *altricial* birds have a relatively shorter period of incubation and lay proportionately smaller eggs. The number of species of altricial birds is much greater than that of precocial birds.

Figure 7

Just as nesting places and nest materials vary widely so there are many sizes and colors of eggs. Bird eggs are beautiful. Years ago it was popular to collect them. Now, except for some major scientific project, one cannot find adequate excuse to thus deplete our already too small bird population. This nesting period is likely the most hazardous time in the life of the bird and the day when the young fledglings first leave the nest is probably the supremely critical day in the whole life cycle. The matter of nest materials, location, egg coloring and incubation habits are very much attuned to safety measures.

Many birds rear but one brood of young each year, some others two, and a few birds up to five or six broods. The number of eggs laid for a *clutch* varies from one for some species up to around 20 with the Bob-white and some other birds. Long before man became such a disturbing factor in Nature these numbers of eggs and broods had likely been correctly adjusted to maintain a fairly uniform balance. Some commercial operation has all too frequently thrown this balance sadly out of line and even resulted in the total extinction of some species.

HOW TO STUDY BIRDS

The best way to acquaint ones self with any group of living things is to get out into their native habitat and observe these plants or animals carefully. In favorable regions some birds may be found at any hour. Early morning from the break of day to two or three hours later is likely the best time of all; next best is in the late afternoon.

When birds have young they are kept busy about all the day feeding them and are much in evidence to the quiet careful observer. A little practice in imitating the distress call of a young bird should make any one sufficiently proficient in this deceit that he can start a panic in bird land. Compressing the lips or holding them against the back of the hand and drawing in air will with a little experience produce the desired *squeak*. It's a mean trick to play on the already nervous parents but when dozens of birds of several species unite to challenge the common foe, one has a grand opportunity to study them at close range. (Fig. 8).

Figure 8

Equipment

When going on a bird trip wear inconspicuous clothes and move quietly. One needs his bird manual, a note book, colored pencils and good field glasses. If buying field glasses do not try to economize too much unless you must. The wide field prism binoculars are well worth the extra cost. High magnification sounds good but makes the glasses very difficult to handle as moving birds are hard to locate and very easily get out of the field of vision. Glasses of around 6 X magnification give good results for most purposes. Compare several glasses and note the difference in the width of field that can be seen at the same distance. The wider the field, the easier it is to locate and hold your bird. Poor glasses often separate the colors in a most annoying way.

If a bird is seen which you cannot positively identify, make a quick outline sketch and put in color, its more distinctive markings. That practice directs one's observation and gives an accurate record to study after the bird is gone (Fig. 9). Look sharply for distinctive characters; then look again and again. Study any peculiar mannerisms the bird possesses. Birds often have characters of flight of other movements that are as distinctive as their color. Make and keep lists of

Figure 9

the birds you see with some record of where and when the observations were made, conditions of weather, temperature etc. A collection of such lists covering a long period of time have high scientific value.

If one follows the plan of neatly noting on the margins of this book the place and date he sees a less common bird, his manual takes on added value from trip to trip and serves to arouse many pleasant memories. It would become much too cumbersome if common birds were thus recorded. A note book may be ruled up with special spaces provided for the various desirable data and columns to serve for several trips or for many years. "A Field Notebook for Studying Birds" especially designed for this purpose with bird names and other matter printed in may be bought at a nominal price.

One soon learns the most favorable spots in his region for finding birds and will be surprised to note how often year after year some fairly rare birds may be found at the same place.

Bird Calls

It is a fine art to be able to recognize birds by their song or call. Many efforts have been made to put bird songs into words. A few birds like the "Bob-white", Dickcissel and Oven-bird have calls so distinctive that almost everybody can agree on what they seem to say. If one chooses his own word phrase for a bird call it makes for him an excellent memory guide but if he should write the phrase out for someone it would likely have less value. For example; some years ago we worked out the phrase *"See-Peter, see-Newt"* for the song of the Western Meadowlark and matched it in inflection many times as we listened to the bird sing. We have found it quite satisfying in comparing that call with the song of our Eastern Meadowlark. We've often told it to students and others but never found anyone who seemed to see much help in our pet phrase.

Anyone with a knack for remembering sounds can learn to recognize the calls of many of our birds. The Allen bird records which are actual recordings of birds in their native habitats are excellent and highly helpful. The "bird songs" of many soloists on the other hand while often pleasing, may not sound at all like the birds they are supposed to imitate.

Camera vs. Gun

To photograph birds requires some special equipment and considerable skill and patience. It is a fine hobby for one who has a flair in

9

Figure 10

that direction and is much better than using a gun.

Some artificial or natural barricade in which the observer can conceal himself is often desirable for studying or photographing birds at the feeding grounds or nesting site. Even a green umbrella with drapes may be set up near a nest and in a day or two the birds will pay little or no attention to it. A few tree branches placed on top will improve it. Such "bird blinds" make possible, photographic shots one could scarcely get otherwise (Fig. 10).

Much of our more exact classification of bird families is based on the internal structure of the birds. For ready and popular identification of species a knowledge of a few external character should get one well started. Here are two bird outlines with some of the more important parts marked (Fig. 11). They should be examined until understood then referred to from time to time. Some of these same terms are pictured and described in the "Index and Pictured Glossary" at the back of the book.

Size of Birds

It will be noted that the size of each species is given. L. (total length) is measured from tip of bill to tip of tail as the dead bird lies gently stretched out on its back. A living bird standing "at attention" does not seem this long. W. (wing length) is measured from the bend of the wing to the tip of the primaries. T. (tail length) which we have given only where some comparisons seem to make it desirable, is measured from the place of insertion to the tip of the longest feather. All these measurements are in inches.

The measurements given have come from various sources and in most cases should be understood to be averages from which there might be as much as 10% deviation or in a few cases even more. Male birds often measure somewhat larger than their mates though this is not true with all species.

In the field it is often desirable to compare a bird's size with some well known bird. The English Sparrow, Robin and Crow are often used in this way. If one will memorize the length of these three birds or such others as he may wish to employ as standards it should be helpful.

The Maps

The natural distribution has been made visual by appending a small map to the drawing of the species. Their migratory movements tend

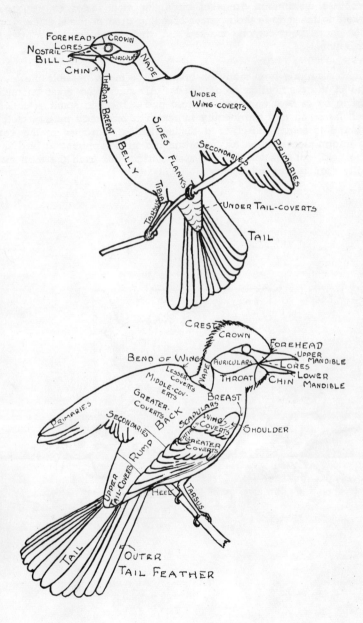

Figure 11. Outlines naming the external parts of birds.

to confuse distribution areas of birds. In most instances the region marked on the map is the summer breeding area of the species. Some of the maps bear regions marked "M" (migration) and "W" (winter distribution).

Numerous reports from many observers have made possible the knowledge of the distribution of our birds. All such data must be understood to be at best only approximate and subject to some variation. It will be noted that the locality in which a bird may be expected to be found is seldom used as a distinguishing character in the keys. This information is often an important aid in determining a bird seen in the field, but it is felt that the user can get this from the map more readily than in any other way.

HOW TO USE THE KEYS

 ith a complete set of bird pictures as here-in given, one can, of course, leaf back and forth until he finds a picture matching the bird he is studying. To run the bird through some simple keys is usually much quicker and the results more reliable.

The statements of these keys are in opposing pairs numbered the same but lettered "a" and "b". By comparing a and b with the bird one usually may be immediately certain which statement applies, then out at the right he finds a number directing him to the pair of statements he should consider next.

By repeating this process of choice and elimination he shortly arrives at the point where his bird is pictured and described. If he has been careful in observing the bird and comparing the statements, he will usually find that the bird before him agrees with the description and picture. If it does not agree then his work has been faulty at some place and he should start over again and watch for his error.

Thus we see a black and white bird with red head hammering on our tree outside our window. Turning to page 14 it is plainly a land bird, 1a which directs us to 2. The bill has no hook at the end so we go to "5". It is plainly not a "chicken-like bird" so we are directed to 6, which in turn sends us to 7. The bill is not very short, very long and slender or grooved so we go by way of 7b, 8b, and 9b to note that our bird agrees with 10b in having two toes turned back and we are then directed to 11a which fits the case and we discover that it is a *Woodpecker* Order *Piciformes* and are referred to page 60.

Figure 12

1a and 1b deals with crests. Our bird has no crest so we go to 3 and note that its head is red, not white. In fact it is wholly red as in 4a and its "belly white" as in 5a. The picture and description found here agree so well with the bird in our tree that we are certain it is a Red-headed Woodpecker.

PICTURED-KEYS FOR IDENTIFYING
THE LAND BIRDS OF NORTH AMERICA

1a Land birds. Feet not webbed. (Fig. 13a)
Legs not unusually long. 2

1b Water birds. With feet webbed for
swimming (Fig. 13b) or with long legs
for wading. (Not treated in this book.
See "How to Know the Water Birds"
(after 1946)).

Figure 13

2a Bill strongly hooked at tip: cere (fleshy or mem-
branous growth) at base of bill. Fig. 14. 3

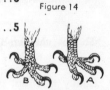

Figure 14

2b Bill without strong hook and cere. 5

3a Toes three in front and one behind (A); the outer front toe often reversible (B). Claws strong,
sharp and curved. Fig. 15. 4

Figure 15

3b Toes permanently two in front and two behind. Lower bill scoop-
shaped. Fig. 16. PARROTS, PAROQUETS. Order *Psittaciformes*.

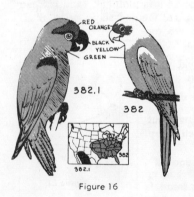

Figure 16

Tropical America has many members
of this family. Only a few of them,
however, have reached our borders
normally. The Carolina Paroquet
once ranging rather widely is now
likely extinct. It was such an unusual bird for our temperate regions
that we describe it here.

382 CAROLINA PAROQUET. Conur-
óptsis carolinénsis carolinénsis
L. 10.5; W. 7.4. Head and neck yellow; cheeks, forehead and shoulders orange; elsewhere bright green.

382.1 THICK-BILLED PARROT. *Rhynchopsitta pachyrhýncha*
L. 16.5; W. 10. Green with red forehead and heavy black bill. This is
the only parrot that resides within
our continental borders and it is
quite rare.

14

4a Eyes at front of head and surrounded by feathered disks. Fig. 17. OWLS.

Order *Strigiformes* page 41

Figure 17

4b Eyes at sides of head, not surrounded by feather disks, plumage compact. Fig. 18. BIRDS OF PREY. Order *Falconiformes* page 17

Figure 18

5a Chicken-like scratching birds with short stout bills and short wings. Hind toe short and noticeably elevated above the others. Fig. 19. GALLINACEOUS BIRDS. Order *Galliformes* page 29

5b Not chicken-like scratching birds. 6

Figure 19

6a Bill very short; mouth large and wide and surrounded by heavy bristles; plumage fluffy, brownish; active for most part at night. Fig. 20. NIGHT-HAWKS, WHIP-POOR-WILLS, etc.

Order *Caprimulgiformes* page 49

Figure 20

6b Feathers compact; hind toe on level with others; and otherwise not as in 6a. 7

7a Bill very short, mouth wide but without bristles surrounding the mouth; active by day. Fig. 21.

SWIFTS. Family *Micropodidae* page 52

7b Not altogether as in 7a. 8

Figure 21

8a Bill very long and slender; tiny swift flying birds of brilliant iridescent plumage (hind toe not much elevated). Fig. 22.

HUMMINGBIRDS. Family *Trochilidae* page 53

Figure 22

15

8b Not as in 8a. 9

9a Bill deeply grooved. Nostril openings
covered with a soft, fleshy membrane.
Fig. 23. PIGEONS AND DOVES. Order
Columbiformes page 36

Figure 23

9b Nostrils not as in 9a. 10

10a Toes three in front, one behind. See Fig. 13A. 13

10b Toes two in front, two behind (A) (rarely only one behind, B).
Fig. 24. 11

11a Climbing birds with heavy chisel-like
bills and stiff tail-feathers for propping. Often, especially the males, with
.red on head. Fig. 24C.
WOODPECKERS. Order *Piciformes*
page 60

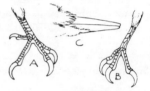

Figure 24

11b Not as in 11a. 12

12a Plumage brown and white or wholly
iridescent black (Ani.); fourth toe
turned back (outer hind toe 3 jointed).
Fig. 25A. CUCKOOS, etc.
Order *Cuculiformes* page 39

Figure 25

12b Plumage brilliantly colored and iridescent; second toe turned back
(inner hind toe 3 jointed). Figs. 25B and 26.
THE TROGONS. Order *Trogoniformes*

BLACK
METALIC
GREEN OR
BRONZE
GREEN
WHITE
RED

389

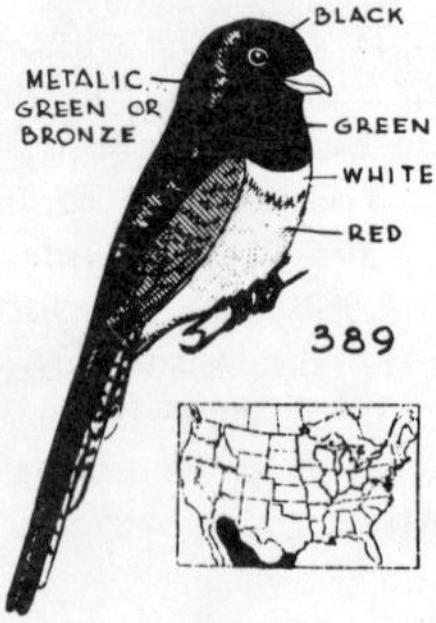

Figure 26

389 COPPERY-TAILED TROGON. *Trogon am-*
biguus ambiguus.
L. 11.3; W. 5.3 ♂ Crown partly or wholly black;
neck, back, scapulars and wing-covers varying
shades of metallic greens or bronzes; tail cop-
pery with black tip and white at sides; chest
greenish bronze with a white stripe separating
it from the red underparts. Bill yellow. ♀ Paler
and more brownish than male. Underparts paler
red.

13a Middle and outer toes joined for half their length, legs small. Bill straight, sharp pointed and longer than the head. Usually rather bright colored. Fig. 27.
KINGFISHERS. Order *Coraciiformes* page 59

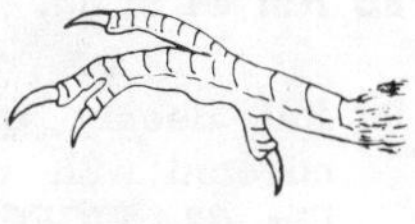

Figure 27

13b Normal perching birds. Hind toe as large as middle one; the nail often longer than middle nail. Tail of 12 feathers. (A very large order including about 2/3 of all the birds of this book.) Fig. 28.
PERCHING BIRDS. Order *Passeriformes* page 69

Figure 28

BIRDS OF PREY. Order *Falconiformes*

(Many of the Hawks are highly variable in color and marking and appear at more than one place in the keys. They are a difficult group.)

1a Head and part of neck naked and appearing small; nostrils large passing through the bill; toenails relatively weak.
THE VULTURES. Figs. 29-31. 2

1b Head proportionately larger, feathered. 4

2a Of eagle size; head orange; broad white stripe on under wing. (Very rare.) Fig. 29.
324 CALIFORNIA CONDOR. *Gýmnogyps californiánus*

YELLOW ORANGE

WHITE

324

L. 50; Wingspread to 11 ft. Body plumage dull blackish; tail and wings black, the latter with a white bar; under wing-coverts wholly white. Young birds lack this white band and have black heads. This and the South American Condor which are substantially the same size are the largest flying birds now living. It does not kill its food and its claws are too weak to carry animals aloft.

Figure 29

2b Smaller vultures. Not over 30 inches long. 3

Figure 30

3a Head red (black in young birds); tail long and relatively slim. Fig. 30. 325 TURKEY VULTURE. *Cathártes áura septentrionális*

L. 30; W. 22, spreading 6 ft. T. 11. Upper parts black with iridescence of purple and green; brownish-black below; head with markings of blue and white in addition to red; feet flesh colored. Most frequently seen soaring in search of carrion, at which times the tips of the wings are held higher than the shoulders.

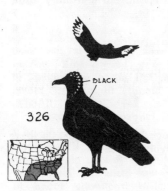

Figure 31

3b Head black; tail short and broad; white patch on under side of wing. Fig. 31. 326 BLACK VULTURE *Córagyps atrátus atrátus*

L. 24; W. 17, spreading over 4 ft. T. 8. Plumage glossy black; shafts of primaries white; legs grayish white, claws black; skin of head much roughened; under wing-coverts white.
Often seen in large numbers in towns and country side of our South where it is protected by law.

Figure 32

4a Throat, neck and entire under parts white, blackish above; Fig. 32. 364 OSPREY *Pandíon haliãётus carolinénsis*

L. 24; W. 18, spreading to 6 ft. Head marked with blackish as pictured; back, wings and tail blackish-brown with purplish sheen. Breast of male with a few brown spots, more numerous on female. Underparts otherwise, wholly white.
This large hawk lives on fish which it catches with its feet. This subspecies ranges throughout the Western Hemisphere. The species is world wide in its distribution.

4b Not as in 4a. **5**

18

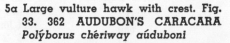

Figure 33

5a Large vulture hawk with crest. Fig. 33. **362 AUDUBON'S CARACARA** *Polýborus chériway aúduboni*

L. 23; Upper parts except neck and tail blackish; throat, entire neck and under wing tips white; upper breast whitish, barred with black; belly black, tail dull whitish with blackish bars; feet yellow, claws black; legs long.

This noisy quarrelsome waste-land bird is usually a carrion feeder but also robs other birds of their legitimate catches.

5b Without a crest. 6

6a Eagle sized bird; 30 inches or more in length; bill unusually large and strong. 7

6b Smaller. Hawks. 8

Figure 34

7a Legs with feathers to the toes; head and body dark golden brown; tail white or grayish at base, broadly tipped with black. Fig. 34. **349 GOLDEN EAGLE.** *Áquila chrysáëtos canadénsis.*

L. 30-36; W. 23-25, spreading up to 7 ft. Great dark golden brown bird; bill bluish; legs yellow; claws black. The immature birds are larger and darker. Most frequently found in mountains where its food consists of rodents and some birds.

351 GRAY SEA EAGLE. *Haliaéetus albicílla.* Light brown head, yellow bill; grayish body, and white tail, inhabits Greenland.

Figure 35

7b Lower part of leg bare; head and tail of adults white. Fig. 35. **352 SOUTHERN BALD EAGLE.** *Haliaéetus leucocéphalus leucocéphalus.*

L. 30-40; W. 22-26, spreading to 7 ft. Adults: Head, neck, tail-coverts and tail white, wings nearly black, remainder of plumage dark brown. Immature: For first 3 years head and tail brown showing some white in third year.

352a NORTHERN BALD EAGLE. *H. l. alascanus.* Similarly marked; larger than 352.

8a A fairly large slim hawk, plainly marked with white rump; wings not pointed. Fig. 36. 331 MARSH HAWK. *Circus hudsonius*.

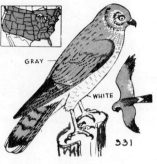

Figure 36

L. 19-22; W. 13.5-15. ♂ Above gray; tail silvery gray, irregularly barred with blackish; upper breast light gray, white below, spotted or barred with rufous. ♀ Brownish above, underparts buff, streaked with brownish. It usually flies low in hunting. Its prey, largely rodents, is eaten at the place it is captured. It has been estimated that one pair of these valuable birds will catch a thousand field mice in one nesting season.

8b Not as in 8a. 9

9a Rounded wings. See Figs. 38 and 39. . .10

9b Pointed wings. Fig. 37. 23

Figure 37

10a Tail long and relatively slim; wings short; low quick flyers. Fig. 38. 21

10b Tail broad and rounded; wings broad; high soaring birds. Fig. 39. 11

Figure 38

11a Breast and belly one color, without spots, streaks or bars. 12

11b Breast or belly streaked or barred. 16

12a Breast black or blackish. 13
   (See also # 337, 342, 344, 347a and 348 each having a dark phase which would throw such individual birds here.)

Figure 39

12b Breast and belly white or whitish. (See also # 342.) 15

13a Wing-coverts black like rest of wing. 14

20

13b Wing-coverts and thighs chestnut; rump and narrow tail-tip white. Fig. 40. 335 HARRIS'S HAWK. *Parabùteo unicinctus hárrisi.*

Figure 40

L. 19-22; W. 13.3-14.5. Blackish-brown; base of tail and upper tail-coverts white; tail rather narrowly tipped with white; lesser wing-coverts and underwing-coverts rufous.

It is a rather tame bird, and flies slowly except when chasing its prey. When hunting it flies low. It is said to join with the Vultures and the Caracaras of its region in eating carrion. It nests in trees or bushes and lays 2 - 4 whitish eggs.

14a Tail with broad band at center, and narrow tip white. Fig. 41. 345 MEXICAN BLACK HAWK. *Urubitinga anthracína anthrácina.*

Figure 41

L. 20-23. Coal black with white tip and broad white band midway in tail; under side of wing with white spot near tip. Young birds lighter, with rusty patches. They invade our region in only limited numbers and live a secluded life. The area of its range and its habits are much like the following (#340). Of course, both of these birds are known in our region only in their extreme northern range.

14b Tail narrowly white tipped with 3 white margined slate crossbands. Fig. 42. 340 ZONE-TAILED HAWK. *Búteo albonotátus.*

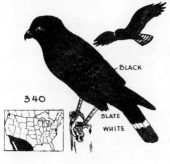

Figure 42

L. 19-21. Glossy black except white and slate markings on tail. The three slate tail-bands become successively wider from base to tip. Each is narrowly margined with white, the white tail-tip, making a fourth cross band. It is a somewhat slimmer built bird than 345. This resident of our Southwest frequents the canons and streams of its area. It feeds on insects, reptiles and small mammals.

21

Figure 43

15a Large hawk with lesser wing-coverts reddish brown. Fig. 43. **341 SENNETT'S WHITE-TAILED HAWK.** *Búteo albicaudátus hypospódius.*

L. 22-24. Ashy-gray to brownish above, with reddish-brown on bend of wing. White tail with rather broad black band near tip, sometimes faintly barred beneath; upper throat dark; remainder of underparts white; sides lightly barred.

Figure 44

15b Small hawk without red-brown patch on wings. Fig. 44. **344 SHORT-TAILED HAWK.** *Búteo brachyúrus.*

L. 17; W. 12.5. Slate-grey above; tail gray with bars of black and with white tip; throat, under wing-coverts, breast and belly white. There is a dark phase with all underparts except tail (including under wing-coverts blackish). The young birds are brownish-black above and buff below and have no black markings.

16a Underparts marked more or less with cross-bars. 18

16b Underparts without cross-bars but marked at least in part with spots or vertical streaks. 17
(Immature birds of #339, 342 and 343 would fall here, also.)

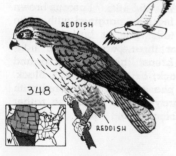

Figure 45

17a Leg feathered in front to toes; tail grayish-white. Fig. 45. **348 FERRUGINOUS ROUGH-LEG.** *Búteo regális.*

L. 20-23; W. 15-17. Grayish-brown above; underparts white or buffy with blackish streaks or spots; legs rufous, barred with black; tail margined with rufous. The dark phase has the same light tail but is quite dark brown both above and below. This hawk is a sluggish flyer.

Figure 46

17b Part of leg bare; tail bright rufous. Fig. 46. 337 EASTERN RED-TAILED HAWK. *Búteo boreális boreális*.

L. 22; W. 16. Dark brown above with mottling of white and gray; white below more or less streaked with blackish on abdomen (sometimes with cross bars); tail bright rust-red above, often with a black band near tip. The tail is gray rather than red on immature birds.

337a KRIDER'S HAWK. *B. b. kríderi.* Lighter colored, sometimes with white head.

337b WESTERN RED-TAILED HAWK. *B. b. calúrus.* Much darker than 337, the abdomen often with heavy dark bars.

337d HARLAN'S HAWK. *B. b. hárlani.* Very dark, almost black; tail much mottled with black, rufous and white. In range it overlaps 337 from Kansas South to the Gulf.

337f FLORIDA RED-TAILED HAWK. *B. b. umbrínus.* Darker above than 337 with chocolate brown stripes and bands on abdomen.

Figure 47

18a Legs feathered in front to toes; belly with black band. Fig. 47. 347a AMERICAN ROUGH-LEGGED HAWK. *Buteo lagópus s.johánnis*.

L. 20-23; W. 15.5-16.5. Fuscous-brown above, the feathers margined with white and buff; tail white or buff for basal half, two or three bars on other half; throat and breast light with streaks and spots of black; belly barred with black. The black phase has a tail barred with white or gray and is otherwise rather uniformly black.

18b Legs partly naked above toes; belly lighter. 19

19a Conspicuous rusty band across breast. **Fig. 48. 342 SWAINSON'S HAWK.** *Búteo swaínsoni.*

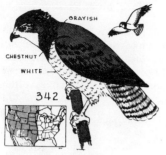

Figure 48

L. 20-22; W. 15-16. Fuscous-brown above with margins of buff and reddish; primaries not barred; the first three notched; belly white or buff with dark streaks, spots or bars. This species is highly variable. The dark phase is almost wholly dark brown.

Its food consists of rodents, seasoned with grasshoppers and crickets. It seems to have a good record for being on friendly terms with other birds.

19b Without a distinct band on breast. **20**

Figure 49

20a Lesser wing-coverts chestnut or reddish-brown. **Fig. 49.**
339 NORTHERN RED-SHOULDERED HAWK. *Búteo lineátus lineátus.*

L. 18-20; W. 13-14. Dark reddish-gray-brown above; first four primaries notched and barred black and white; tail dark with four or five white bars and a white tip.

339a FLORIDA RED-SHOULDERED HAWK. *B. l. álleni.* Smaller with grayish white head.

339b RED-BELLIED HAWK. *B. l. élegans.* Under parts largely bright rusty red.

339d TEXAS RED-SHOULDERED HAWK. *B. l. texánus.*

Figure 50

20b Lesser wing-coverts dark grayish brown; tail with three narrow grayish-white bars. **Fig. 50.**
343 BROAD-WINGED HAWK. *Búteo platýpterus platýpterus.*

L. 14-18; W. 10.5-12. Head blackish-brown, the back more grayish; tail grey-brown with three whitish bars; throat white; breast pale yellowish-brown thickly marked with triangular red-brown spots or bars; first three primaries notched but without bars.

21a Smaller than a crow; marked on under side with rusty brown bars. 22

334

Figure 51

21b Larger than a crow; white line over eye; under parts with blackish streaks. Fig. 51. 334 EASTERN GOSHAWK. *Astur atricapíllus atricapíllus.*

L. 23; W. 13. Bluish-slate above; head darker; outer tail feathers with reddish tinge, tipped with white; under parts white with wavy gray cross lines. A persistent and seemingly fearless hunter.

334a WESTERN GOSHAWK. *A. a. striátulus.* Darker above and with more markings on the underparts.

346 MEXICAN GOSHAWK. *Asturnía plagiáta plagiáta.* A smaller bird (L. 17.) is really not a Goshawk. No white line on head; tail with 3 or 4 white or black cross-bars.

333

Figure 52

22a Tail rounded; larger than 332. Fig. 52. 333 COOPER'S HAWK. *Accípiter coóperi.*

L. 15.5-19; W. 9.5-10.5. Slate-gray above, top of head blackish; under parts white with rusty brown bars; immature birds more brownish; tail and underwings barred.

Often highly destructive to poultry and other birds.

22b Tail square cut at end; smaller than preceeding. Fig. 53. 332 SHARP-SHINNED HAWK. *Accípiter vélox vélox.*

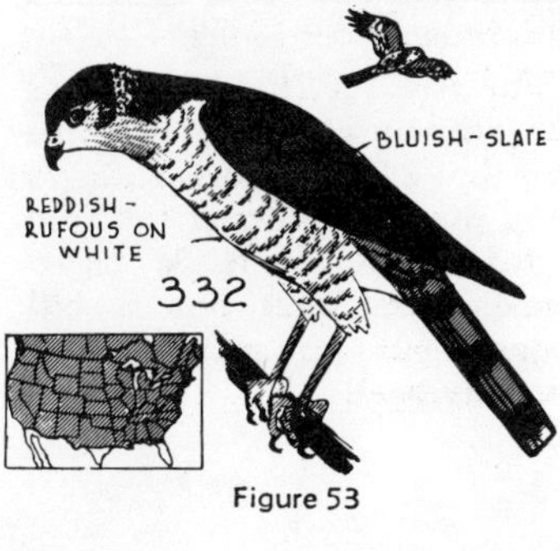

332

Figure 53

L. 11.3-13.5; W. 7-8. Appears in coloring and marks to be a small edition of Cooper's hawk. The crown while darker than the body is not so dark as in 333.

Too small to successfully handle larger poultry, it takes a serious toll of small birds.

23a Scales on front of tarsus, square. KITES. Figs. 54-56. 24

23b Scales on front of tarsus, rounded. FALCONS. Figs. 57-61. 26

24a Tail square cut at end. 25

24b Tail deeply forked. Fig. 54.

327 SWALLOW-TAILED KITE. *Elanoídes forficátus forficátus.*

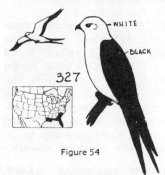

Figure 54

L. 24; W. 16.5. Head, neck, under side of wings, rump and under parts white, other feathered parts shining bluish-black.

It spends much of its time in the air and is rated as the most graceful of birds. It feeds on reptiles, insects and amphibians which it often carries aloft and consumes as it flies.

25a Tail white. Fig. 55.

328 WHITE-TAILED KITE. *Elánus leucúrus majúsculus.*

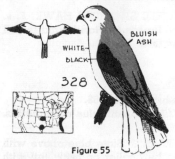

Figure 55

L. 15.5; W. 12.5. Ashy-gray above, crown lighter; shoulders black; tail and under parts white. The immature birds are rusty above.

It adds to the diet of 327 an occasional small bird. It's nest of stick and leaves is placed high up in trees.

25b Tail black. Fig. 56.

329 MISSISSIPPI KITE. *Ictínia misisippiénsis.*

Figure 56

L. 14; W. 11.3. Head, neck, a broad wing-bar and under parts gray; back bluish-slate; primaries with markings of reddish-brown; tail black.

330 EVERGLADE KITE. *Rostrhámus sociábilis plúmbeus.* Larger than the preceding (L. 18.), it is darker above with rump, base and tip of tail and under parts white. It feeds on a fresh water snail and has a bill shaped just right for removing its prey from the shell.

26a About the size of a crow or larger. **28**

26b Only a little larger than a robin. **27**

27a Back and especially the tail, bright rufous-red. Fig. 57.
    360 EASTERN SPARROW HAWK. *Fálco sparvérius sparvérius.*

Figure 57

L. 10; W. 7.5. ♂ Back reddish, sparingly barred with black; tail reddish with white tip and rather broad black band; head slate blue; crown with reddish spot; wing-coverts bluish; under parts buff with a few blackish spots. ♀ Wing-coverts reddish, barred with black; back and tail with many more bars than in ♂; under parts with brownish streaks.

360a DESERT SPARROW HAWK. *F. s. phaláéna.* A bit larger than 360 and noticeably lighter colored.

360c LITTLE SPARROW HAWK. *F. s. paúlus.* Breeds in Florida and is still smaller than 360.

27b Back and tail slate blue or blackish-brown. Fig. 58.
    357 EASTERN PIGEON HAWK. *Fálco columbárius columbárius.*

Figure 58

L. 12; W. 8. ♂ Slate blue above with obscure buff collar on neck; tail with grayish white bars and tipped with white; under parts buff. ♀ and immature birds are brownish above with buffish bars on tail.

357a BLACK PIGEON HAWK. *F. c. súckleyi.* Black in the throat and darker throughout.

357b RICHARDSON'S PIGEON HAWK. *F. c. ríchardsoni.* Has five dark bands on its tail and is generally lighter colored than 357.

357c WESTERN PIGEON HAWK. *F. c. béndirei.*

28a With black "mustache" streak on lower face; upper parts dark bluish slate. Fig. 59.

Figure 59

356a DUCK HAWK. *Fálco peregrínus ánatum.*
L. 16-20; W. 12.5-14. Dark bluish-slate above; tail with white tip and obscure black bars; underparts buff, specked and barred with black. Immature birds show fuscous above.

356b PEALE'S FALCON. *F. p. peálei.* Similar but darker colored.

359 APLOMADO FALCON. *F. túscocoeruléscens septentrionális.*. Somewhat smaller than the Duck Hawk, has a rufous band around its crown and a wide black band across the belly. It is very rare within our borders.

28b Not marked as in 28a. 29
29a Reddish-brown above; white below with many brown spots. Fig. 60.   **355 PRAIRIE FALCON.** *Fálco mexicánus.*

Figure 60

L. 17; W. 12.2. Above brownish-ash with markings of buff; primaries dark brown; tail lighter with tip of white; face with brown "mustache".

Ground squirrels seem to afford it most of its food. Its nest is usually on a rocky cliff.

29b Upper parts white (or blackish); a very large northern falcon. Fig. 61.   353 WHITE GYRFALCON. *Fálco rustícolus cándicans.*

Figure 61

L. 22; W. 16. Plumage wholly white, the feathers of wing-coverts and back with a variable number of pale gray spots; bill and feet bluish; eyes brown with blue lids.

354b BLACK GYRFALCON. *F. r. obsolétus.* Dusky or brownish-slate, darker below, the feathers narrowly margined with buff.

Various color phases intermediate between these two exist. These birds belong to the Arctic region and reach our areas only in winter.

28

GALLINACEOUS BIRDS. Order *Galliformes*

1a Head and neck at least in part feathered. 2

1b Large birds with head and upper neck naked. Fig. 62.
    310a EASTERN TURKEY. *Meleágris gallopávo silvéstris.*

310A

Figure 62

L. ♂ 48, ♀ 37; W. ♂ 21, ♀ 16. The naked head and upperneck, usually pink or red with purple and blue areas, is wrinkled and wattled and has an erectile process (often quite long in ♂) ♂ Lower neck, back and breast dark brownish-green, much bronzed and highly iridescent; tail dark brownish with cross-bars of black; tip of tail chestnut; a "beard" of coarse black hairs hangs from its upper breast. ♀ Duller colored with less metallic sheen.

310b FLORIDA TURKEY. *M. g. osceóla* is smaller. The bars on the primaries are smaller and more broken.

310c RIO GRANDE TURKEY. *M. g. intermédia* of the same size as 310a but with buff on tip of tail.

310 MERRIAM'S TURKEY. *M. g. mérriami* differs from the three above in having a white tipped tail as in our domestic turkey.
A Mexican form was taken to Europe and domesticated early in the 16th century. Our Common Turkey comes from this stock.

2a Without bare patches on both throat and face. 3

2b Face and throat patch bare; head with crest. Fig. 63.
    311 CHACHALACA. *Órtalis vétula vétula.*

311

Figure 63

L. 22; W. 8; T. 11. Dark greenish-brown above; paler and tinged with brownish-yellow below tail long, green, tipped at sides with white.

It lives on the ground, is shy, nests in bushes and is very noisy. They seem to repeat their name in a harsh trumpeting voice.

29

3a Fairly large long-tailed birds; male brilliantly colored. Fig. 64.

   309.1 RING-NECKED PHEASANT. *Phasiánus cólchicus torquátus.*

Figure 64

L. ♂ 35, ♀ 20; T. ♂ 20, ♀ 12. ♂ Head and neck purplish-green with white ring separating it from the black and white speckled back and breast. The entire bird with many colors and much iridescence. ♀ Tawny, mottled with black and white. This hybrid of two exotic species is widely introduced in our country and prized by sportsmen. South Dakota claims it as its state bird.

Several species of imported Pheasants are reared in captivity, the Golden and the Lady Amherst likely being the best known.

The PEACOCK. *Pávo cristátus.*, a close relative of the pheasants, comes from Southern Asia.

3b Not as in 3a. 4

4a Tarsus bare. QUAILS. Figs. 73-79. 12

4b Tarsus covered at least in part with feathers. 5

5a Not entirely white or without large white areas. 6

5b Entire bird wholly white in winter; in summer the tail, lower breast and wings are white. Fig. 65.

   304c SOUTHERN WHITE-TAILED PTARMIGAN.
   Lagópus leucúrus altípetens.

Figure 65

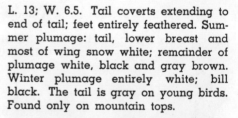

L. 13; W. 6.5. Tail coverts extending to end of tail; feet entirely feathered. Summer plumage: tail, lower breast and most of wing snow white; remainder of plumage white, black and gray brown. Winter plumage entirely white; bill black. The tail is gray on young birds. Found only on mountain tops.

304b RAINIER WHITE-TAILED PTARMIGAN. *L. l. rainierénsis.* is similar to above.

301 WILLOW PTARMIGAN. *L. lygópus álbus.* L. 16. Brownish in summer; white with blackish tails in winter; mottled white and brown, spring and fall.

6a Breast or belly or both with large patches of black. 7

6b Breast and under parts light brownish or grayish. 10

7a Large gray brown birds with black belly and spreading, pointed tail feathers. Fig. 66.

Figure 66

309 SAGE HEN. *Centrocérus urophasiánus.*

L. ♂ 28; ♀ 20. ♂ Mottled grayish-brown above. Chin and throat blackish with yellowish-white face and naked patch on neck of yellow skin which may be distended. Under parts black as pictured. ♀ Lighter colored and much smaller than male; no special structures on neck.

A bird of the open country.

7b Smaller birds; smooth edged tails. 8

8a Tail tipped with orange brown or slate gray. 9

8b Tail not lighter tipped. Fig. 67.

299 FRANKLIN'S GROUSE. *Canachítes fránklini.*

L. 16; W. 6.5. ♂ Dusky gray to blackish; alternating black and white bands on sides of rump; tail not lighter tipped. ♀ Lighter sooty gray than male; tail-coverts white tipped and tail also tipped with white.

This bird as well as one or two others of its near relatives has been dubbed "Fool Hen". They seem to have but little sense of fear and may often be knocked down with a stick in the hand.

Figure 67

9a Tail black with orange-brown band at end; sides barred with black and white. Fig. 68.

298c CANADA SPRUCE GROUSE. *Canachítes canadénsis cánace.*

L. 17. ♂ Dusky slate-colored above with considerable black; rufous on wings; patch of naked yellow or reddish skin above eye. ♀ Brown above mottled with tawny and with black cross-bars; under parts lighter; flanks streaked with white; tail with narrow orange-brown tip.

298 HUDSONIAN SPRUCE GROUSE. *C. c. canadénsis.* Closely similar to the former.

Figure 68

31

9b Tail black, tipped with light gray; sides uniformly light gray.
Fig. 69.   **297 DUSKY GROUSE.** *Dendrágapus obscúrus obscúrus.*

L. 18-22. ♂ Slaty-black above; bluish-gray below; tail fan-shaped; naked skin over eye yellow. ♀ Dusky black mottled with brown; sides with mixed transverse bars of yellowish-brown.

297b RICHARDSON'S GROUSE. *D. o. ríchardsoni.* Darker than 297, with no terminal band on tail.

297a SOOTY GROUSE. *D. fulginósus fulginósus.* Darker than 297, with light tipped tail; inhabits forests.

Figure 69

10a With short dark tail white banded at tip; a prairie bird. Fig. 70.
305 GREATER PRAIRIE CHICKEN. *Tympanúchus cupído americánus.*

L. 18. Yellowish-brown above with spottings of black; white with dusky-brown bars below. A tuft of stiff feathers (considerably larger and darker in ♂) on side of neck covering a naked patch of yellow skin.

305a ATTWATER'S PRAIRIE CHICKEN. *T. c. áttwateri.* A somewhat smaller and darker bird.

307 LESSER PRAIRIE CHICKEN. *T. pallidicínctus,* similar to 305 but paler.

Figure 70

10b Not as in 10a. 11

11a With long sharp tail; no neck tufts; lighter colored. Fig. 71.
308 NORTHERN SHARP-TAILED GROUSE. *Pedioecétes phasianéllus phasianéllus.*

L. 20. Above gray; whitish below; tail pointed, with middle pair of feathers considerable longer than the others. Tail shorter in ♀.

308a COLUMBIAN SHARP-TAILED GROUSE. *P. p. columbiánus.*

308b PRAIRIE SHARP-TAILED GROUSE. *P. p. campéstris.*

Figure 71

11b Tail long and fan shaped; inhabits the woods. Fig. 72.
    300 EASTERN RUFFED GROUSE. *Bonása umbéllus umbéllus.*

Figure 72

L. 17; W. 7.3. Rufous above variegated with black and white; a large tuft of glossy black feathers at sides of neck (small in ♀); tail banded with black and white. It is the state bird of Pennsylvania.

300a CANADA RUFFED GROUSE. *B. u. togata.* Gray instead of rufous beneath and more definitely barred.

300b GRAY RUFFED GROUSE. *B. u. umbelloídes.* Grayer than 300.

300c OREGON RUFFED GROUSE. *B. u. sábini.* Darker and redder than the others.

12a Eastern birds. 13
12b Western birds. 14
13a Reddish-brown back, mottled light beneath. Fig. 73.
    289 EASTERN BOB-WHITE. *Colínus virginiánus virginiánus.*

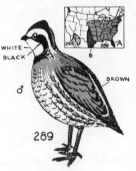

Figure 73

L. 10; W. 4.5. Head of ♂ black and white; ♀ black and buff. Tail ashy-gray; under parts white, barred with black. It's easily recognized whistled call gives it its name. Both Rhode Island and Oklahoma have named the Bob-white their state bird.

289a FLORIDA BOB-WHITE. *C. v. floridánus.* Smaller and darker than 289.

289b TEXAS BOB-WHITE. *C. v. texánus.* Grayer than 289 and smaller.

291 MASKED BOB-WHITE. *C. rídgwayi.* ♂ Forehead, face and throat black; top and back of head dark; long white line frequently over eye; breast bright chestnut. ♀ Similar to Texas Bob-white.

13b Tail, broad crescent on breast and bars on sides chestnut. Fig. 74.
    288.1 EUROPEAN PARTRIDGE. *Pérdix pérdix pérdix.*

Figure 74

L. 12-14. Upper parts and chest gray; large chestnut crescent on breast with prominent white spot below. The reddish tail is very conspicuous in flight. Rather widely introduced as a game bird.

14a Pale blue-gray with fluffy white crest. Fig. 75.
293 ARIZONA SCALED QUAIL. *Callipépla squamáta pállida.*

Figure 75

L. 10-12. Feathers of under parts light gray with narrow darker borders giving a scaled effect to the breast. Crest sometimes buffy.

293a CHESTNUT-BELLIED SCALED QUAIL. *C. s. castanogastris.* Similar to the foregoing but with chestnut patch on belly.

These excellent food birds could be very abundant with a little better protection. They rear two or three broods a season and feed largely on insects.

14b Not as in 14a. 15

15a With plume on head. 16

15b Small quail without a plume (but with close lying crest.). Fig. 76.
296 MEARN'S QUAIL. *Cyrtónyx montezúmae meárnsi.*

Figure 76

L. 8. ♂ Crest brown; face black and white as pictured; wings with round black dots. ♀ Upper parts mixed black, tawny and lavender; pale lavender-brown below; head grayish-brown without stripes. Bill heavy in both sexes.

This is another bird so tame that it has been practically exterminated except where raised domestically. It makes excellent eating.

16a Plume short, curving forward. 17

16b Plume long, nearly straight extending up and back. Fig. 77.
292 MOUNTAIN QUAIL. *Oreórtyx pícta pálmeri.*

Figure 77

L. 12. Back, wings, tail and chest olive-brown; throat and abdomen chestnut with white markings as pictured. Plume about 2 inches long, and consists of two feathers.

292a PLUMED QUAIL. *O. p. pícta.* Lighter on back of head and neck.

292b SAN PEDRO QUAIL. *O. p. confínis.* Grayer than either of the above.

These birds rear but one large brood each year. Their food is almost wholly seeds and grain.

34

17a Breast and abdomen of male white with large black spot, flanks reddish. Fig. 78.

295 GAMBEL'S QUAIL. *Lophórtyx gámbeli gámbeli.*

REDDISH

BLACK

BLACK

295

Figure 78

L. 10. ♂ Top of head and sides below wings reddish; upper parts and chest bluish-ash; face black and white. ♀ Top of head grayish-brown; no prominent head markings as on male. Lives in the deserts.

295a OLATHE QUAIL. *L. g. sánus.*

All of the Quails are rapid runners. This species feeds largely on insects and rears broods of about a dozen young.

17b Flanks and back olive-brown breast tawny with chestnut on abdomen. Fig. 79.

294 CALIFORNIA QUAIL. *Lophórtyx califórnica califórnica.*

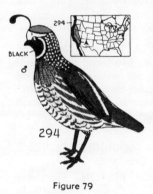

294

BLACK

♂

294

Figure 79

L. 11. ♂ Olive-brown above with numerous white dots on back of neck; head brownish-yellow in front, light brown at back of crown. ♀ Plain olive-gray with white markings. Crest black in both sexes; much shorter in ♀. California claims it as its state bird.

294a VALLEY QUAIL. *L. c. vallícola.* Lighter in color than 294.

Folks in their region are very much in love with these friendly little birds. They are often seen in gardens and thickets and are very tame all summer long.

While they are neither pictured nor keyed it may be helpful to mention some domestic birds which belong to this order.

The GUINEA-FOWL. *Númida meleágris,* is a native of Africa.

The DOMESTIC HEN now developed into very numerous forms and varieties is thought to be a descendent of the RED JUNGLE FOWL. *Gállus gállus* of India. The "Blue Hen" is the state bird of Delaware. One of our major food industries centers around the Domestic Hen. The annual sales of both meat and eggs runs into large figures.

1133475

PIGEONS AND DOVES
Order *Columbiformes*

1a Well known domestic bird with wide variation in color and form.
Fig. 80.   313.1 ROCK DOVE, (DOMESTIC PIGEON).
Colúmba lívia lívia.

L. 12-15. Tail fan-shaped in flight usually blunt at rest; rump white; two black bands on wing; feet and tarsus red.

Artificial selection has produced many color and pattern differences in our domestic pigeons. Many shapes, some rather grotesque have likewise been recognized. Pouter, dragon, fan-tail, trumpeter, homing, barb, etc. are seen at exhibits.

Figure 80

1b Not as in 1a. 2

2a Tail pointed (spike shaped when at rest; broader and showing white patches when flying.) Fig. 81.
316 EASTERN MOURNING DOVE. *Zenaidúra macroúra carolinénsis.*

L. 12; W. 5.8. ♂ Brownish-slate with metallic sheen on head and neck; small black ear-mark on head; middle tail feathers same color as back, others with a black band above the rather broad white tip. ♀ Similar but with less iridescence.

316a WESTERN MOURNING DOVE. Z. m. *marginélla.* Similar to 316.

315 PASSENGER PIGEON. *Ectopístes migratórius.* This once exceedingly abundant and remarkable bird has been extinct for many years. Considerably larger (L. 17) than the Mourning Dove, it was darker and with more iridescence. We give this brief statement so that it will not be "discovered" too often by beginners.

Figure 81

2b Tail not pointed. 3

3a Tail tipped with white. 4

3b Tail without white at tip. 6

4a With white patch on wing. **Fig. 82.**

319 EASTERN WHITE-WINGED DOVE.
Melopelia asiática asiática.

L. 12; Bluish-slate marked with white as pictured. The white wing patches are especially conspicuous in flight. Fairly large black earmark. Key West, Florida.

319a WESTERN WHITE-WINGED DOVE. *M. a. meárnsi.* Quite similar. Note the white tipped rounded tail of both of these birds.

318 WHITE-FRONTED DOVE. *Leptótila fulvivéntris angélica.* (L. 12) White tipped tail and under parts whitish but no white on wings, ranges along the Rio Grande in Southern Texas.

319

Figure 82

4b Wings not marked with white. 5

5a Back of neck with spotted or black band. **Fig. 83.**

315.1 CHINESE SPOTTED DOVE. *Spilopélia chinénsis chinénsis.*

L. 12.5. Brownish-slate with a wide band of black and white dots on neck.

315.2 RINGED TURTLE DOVE. *Streptopélia risória.* L. 12. Pale tan slate with narrow black band on neck.

These two birds are alike in having rounded tails with white corners and in both having been introduced into the Los Angeles area.

Figure 83

5b Neck without band. **Fig. 84.**

321 INCA DOVE. *Scardafélla ínca ínca.*

L. 8. Tawny gray, with scale markings of dusky above and on light under parts. Tail relatively long with white along its sides.

This rather small dove, originally living in the desert was quick to find advantage in associating with man and is often partly domesticated, and very tame. It keeps repeating its cooing calls rather continuously.

321

Figure 84

6a Large bird with white crescent at back of neck and broad pale band at tip of tail. Fig. 85.

312 BAND-TAILED PIGEON. *Colúmba fasciáta fasciáta.*

Figure 85

L. 16. Head and under parts purplish-drab; upper parts brownish-gray and bluish-gray, heavily bronzed; rump light; legs and feet yellow.

The law has spared this large bird the fate of the Passenger Pigeon, for it was once killed in great numbers. It usually lays but one egg so multiplies slowly.

313 RED-BILLED PIGEON. *Colúmba flavirostris flavirostris.* L. 15. A rather uniformly dark slate colored bird; head and neck purplish pink without iridescence. Ranges along the Rio Grande.

6b Our smallest dove; tail short, square cut and tipped with black. Fig. 86.

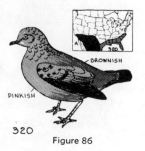

Figure 86

320 EASTERN GROUND DOVE. *Columbigallína passerína passerína.*

L. 6.8; W. 3.6. ♂ Forehead and under parts pink tinged; crown and nape bluish-slate; back brownish; tail dark. ♀ Forehead and under parts pale brownish-gray.

320a MEXICAN GROUND DOVE. *C. p. palléscens.* Similar to above but head, under parts and back paler.

CUCKOO-LIKE BIRDS
Order *Cuculiformes*

1a Bluish-black, bill as high as long, and much compressed. Fig. 87.
384 GROOVE-BILLED ANI. *Crotóphaga sulciróstris sulciróstris.*

384

Figure 87

L. 14.5; W. 5.7. Dull black with purplish or greenish sheen; upper bill with three longitudinal grooves on each side. It is said to feed on the insects it finds on cattle.

383 SMOOTH-BILLED ANI. *Crotophaga ani.* Bill without grooves, but otherwise closely resembles 384. It is tropical but gets into Fla. and has been reported as an accidental visitant in La. and Penn. It is gregarious and several females are said to share on hugh nest.

These birds are distributed throughout Mexico and on down into South America. They lay 3 to 5 pale blue eggs.

1b Bill normal; color not black. 2

2a Large crested bird, as pictured. Fig. 88.
385 ROAD-RUNNER. *Geocóccyx californiánus.*

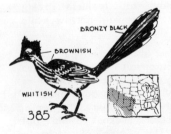

385

Figure 88

L. 23; W. 6.7. Shining olive-brown with feather margins whitish or rusty. Tail large and much rounded; the outer feathers white tipped.

It is very active on foot moving with wings and tail spread at remarkable speed. It feeds on small snakes and on lizards. It is the state bird of New Mexico.

The Road-runners offer a high interest point to the tourist in the West. If they decide to run on ahead of the car instead of crossing the highway their speed can be better appreciated.

2b Slender brownish, solitary birds without crest. 3

3a Outer tail feathers black with large white tip; wing with rusty
patch; lower mandible yellow. Fig. 89.

  387 YELLOW-BILLED CUCKOO. *Coccýzus americánus americánus.*

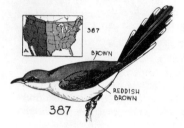

387

Figure 89

L. 12.3; W. 5.7. Grayish-brown above,
outer web of primaries reddish; tail
feathers except middle two, black
marked with white as pictured; under parts white.

The Cuckoos are highly valuable
birds as they eat quantities of hairy
caterpillars, spurned by many other
birds. They are more often heard
than seen. Their characteristic call
has given them the name "Rain
Crow".

387a CALIFORNIA CUCKOO. C. a.
occidentális. Larger, more grayish
and with larger bill.

386a MAYNARD'S CUCKOO. C. mín-
or maýnardi. Under parts buff; sometimes reaches Florida.

4b Bill wholly black; tail brownish-gray with but small white spots at
tip of feathers. Fig. 90.

  388 BLACK-BILLED CUCKOO. *Coccýzus erythrophthálmus.*

388

Figure 90

L. 11.5; W. 5.3. Olive-brown above,
white below; tail feathers except
middle two black with narrow white
tips.

The cuckoos should not be confused
with the European Cuckoo, notorious
for laying its eggs in the nests of
birds of other species and assuming
no further responsibility for repro-
duction. Our cuckoos build flat
Mourning Dove type of nests in
bushes or low trees and lay two or
three dull pale bluish eggs and
hatch and care for their own young
in the approved manner.

OWLS
Order *Strigiformes*

1a Face disk heart-shaped definitely pointed below, white; legs long with feathers on back of tarsus pointing upward; edge of middle toes comb like. Fig. 91.

365 BARN OWL. *Týto álba pratíncola.*

GRAY BUFF & BLACK

365

Figure 91

L. 18; W. 13.5. Upper parts grayish-buff, specked with black and white; tail buff or white often marked with black, under parts white or buff; eyes comparatively small, black; heart-shaped facial disk margined with buff or reddish.

This is a highly valuable bird because of the great quantity of small rodents it consumes. This so called Monkey-faced Owl is likely present in many communities where it is unknown, for its activities are confined to the night time.

1b Face disk usually round, not heart-shaped; feathers if present on back of tarsus, pointing down; edge of middle toe not comb-like. TYPICAL OWLS. Family *Strigidae.* 2

2a With more or less conspicuous ear tufts. 3

2b Without ear tufts. 7

3a Small owls not over 10 inches long. Two color phases red-brown and gray. 4

3b Larger; at least 13 inches long. 5

4a A rare little owl, 7 inches or less in length, found in high mountains; toes naked. Fig. 92.

374 FLAMMULATED SCREECH OWL. *Ótus flamméolus.*

GRAY

374

Figure 92

L. 6.6; W. 5.4. Two distinct color phases, cinnamon brown and brownish-gray; face grayish-white or light brownish; ear tufts small. Under parts white with darker markings; eyes brown.

373.1 SPOTTED SCREECH OWL. *Ótus trichópsis.* Somewhat larger than the preceeding (7-8 inches) distinguished from all other Screech Owls by the white spots on back of neck. Confined in the U. S. to the mountains of southern Arizona.

41

4b Common widely distributed owls up to 10 inches; toes feathered or bristled. Fig. 93.

373m EASTERN SCREECH OWL. Ótus ásio naévius.

L. 8-10; W. 6-7. Bright rufous above or grayish (Most of the western subspecies are always grayish); under parts whitish, ear tufts about one inch long; eyes yellow.

373 SOUTHERN SCREECH OWL. O. a. ásio. Smaller than the above.

373a FLORIDA SCREECH OWL. O. a. floridánus. Small and darker, the reddish phase very rare.

373b TEXAS SCREECH OWL. O. a. mccálli. Paler than the eastern form.

373c CALIFORNIA SCREECH OWL. O. a. béndirei. Rather brownish above, thickly below.

RUFOUS
(OR
GRAYISH)

373d KENNICOTT'S SCREECH OWL. O. a. kénnicotti. Medium sized with two color phases. Belongs principally in Alaska.

373e ROCKY MOUNTAIN SCREECH OWL. O. a. maxwélliae. The lightest colored subspecies; much white in evidence.

373f MEXICAN SCREECH OWL. O. a. cineráceus. Medium sized with densely feathered toes.

373

Figure 93

373g AIKEN'S SCREECH OWL. O. a. aíkeni. Definitely blackish-gray with heavy markings beneath.

373h MAC FARLANE'S SCREECH OWL. O. a. macfarlanei. Fairly large and gray.

373i HASBROUCK'S SCREECH OWL. O. a. hásbroucki. A large, dark, heavily marked subspecies.

373j BREWSTER'S SCREECH OWL. O. a. bre̊wsteri. Dark like the above but still larger.

373k PASADENA SCREECH OWL. O. a. quercínus. With very limited range.

373l SAHAURO SCREECH OWL. O. a. gílmani. A desert living subspecies.

5a Belly with vertical stripes; ear tufts small. About the size of a crow. Fig. 94.

367 SHORT-EARED OWL. *Asio flámmeus flámmeus.*

REDDISH BROWN

L. 14-17; W. 12-13. Upper parts yellowish-brown to buffy, striped with dark brown or blackish, quite variable; tail with alternate bands of buff and brown. Under parts whitish, with brown streaks, eyes yellow.

Lives in grassy marshes where it does its hunting. It flies in an erratic manner. It is sometimes referred to as the Marsh Owl.

Figure 94

5b Belly with cross bars; ear-tufts prominent. 6

6a Smaller, about crow size; grayish in general tone; throat and chest with vertical streaks. Fig. 95.

366 LONG-EARED OWL. *Asio wilsoniánus.*

L. 13-16; W. 10-11.5. Upper surface gray, transversely marked with blackish-brown and grayish-white; ear-tufts dark at middle; face reddish-brown; under parts lighter.

Remains hidden by day, hunting at night; feeds on rodents, most of which are mice. It seldom feeds on birds.

The nest of the Long-Eared Owl is usually in a tree although it sometimes builds on the ground. Nests of squirrels or crows are often remodelled and used. Three to seven white eggs are laid.

Owls are noted for their noiseless flight. Their soft fluffy feathers make this possible. For the most part they are beneficial to man. Bounties have sometimes been paid for their extermination. This usually results in killing off the better species and in an expensive increase of mice and other rodent pests.

Figure 95

6b A very large owl; ear-tufts about 2 inches long; throat with white Y-shaped mark. Fig. 96.

375 GREAT HORNED OWL. *Búbo virginiánus virginiánus.*

L. 20-24; W. 13-15. Upper parts mottled yellowish-buff and black; primaries and tail with bars; facial disk yellowish-buff, eyes yellow; belly with many fine cross-bars; feet and toes feathered, whitish.

375a WESTERN HORNED OWL. *B. v. palléscens.* Pale on face and underparts; feet often unmarked.

375b ARTIC HORNED OWL. *B. v. subárcticus.* With much white and fewer markings. Reaches our mapped area only in winter.

375c DUSKY HORNED OWL. *B. v. saturátus.* Dark both above and below with feet much spotted.

375

375d PACIFIC HORNED OWL. *B. v. pacíficus.* Largely grayish-brown and buffy above; face and underparts rather dark; feet spotted.

375f LABRADOR HORNED OWL. *B. v. heterocnémis.* Dark above, somewhat light below; feet much spotted.

Figure 96

375i NORTHWESTERN HORNED OWL. *B. v. lagophónus.* Rufescent or tawny above.

375j MONTANA HORNED OWL. *B. v. occidentális.* Light colored but not so much so as 375b.

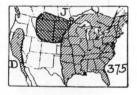

It should be understood that the regions marked on the maps are approximate and that areas frequently overlap.

7a Small earless owls; scarcely larger than a Robin; some of them smaller. **8**

7b Large earless owls the smallest almost as large as a Crow; usually considerably larger. **12**

8a About the size of an English Sparrow. Usually associated with the giant cactus in which it nests. Fig. 97.

     381 WHITNEY'S ELF OWL. *Micropállas whítneyi whítneyi.*

Figure 97

L. 5.5-6; W. 4.4. Two color phases, gray and brown. The gray phase is the more common. "Eyebrows" and bar on shoulders white; tail with several bars; facial disks cinnamon often with buffish tint; underparts mixed black, white and buff.

381a TEXAS ELF OWL. *M. w. idóneus.* Under markings darker but with larger white areas than the above.

8b Somewhat larger than in 8a. 9

9a Throat and chest spotted; lower parts barred; legs rather long and not feathered; lives in burrows in open country; active by day. Fig. 98.

     378 WESTERN BURROWING OWL. *Speótyto cuniculária hypugaéa.*

Figure 98

L. 9.5; W. 7. Above brown, spotted with white and brownish-buff; tail with broken bars of dull buff; under parts lighter buff with brown bars.

It lives and nests in the deserted burrow of a Prairie-dog or other animals or sometimes digs its own burrow.

378a FLORIDA BURROWING OWL. *S. c. floridána.* Grayish-brown above, spotted and barred with white; throat white; under parts barred with gray.

9b Not as in 9a. 10

10a Tail relatively long; two-thirds to three-fourths as long as wing. Fig. 99.

379 ROCKY MOUNTAIN PYGMY OWL. *Glaucídium gnóma pinícola.*

L. 7-7.5; W. 3.8; T. 2.7. Grayish-brown above, with prominent black spot at side of neck, streaked below with blackish. Tail often held up at an angle. When in flight the wings make a whistling sound. It hunts by day.

379a CALIFORNIA PYGMY OWL. *G. g. californicum.* Browner than the above.

379c COAST PYGMY OWL. *G. g. grinnélli.* Reddish brown.

379b VANCOUVER PYGMY OWL. *G. g. swárthi.* Sooty-brown above.

Figure 99

380 FERRUGINOUS PYGMY OWL. *G. brasiliánum rídgwayi.* Smaller and more reddish. Under streakings brown.

10b Tail relatively shorter; barely over half the length of the wing...11

11a Larger; about the size of a Screech Owl. Face whitish with black frame; forehead finely specked with white. Fig. 100.

371 RICHARDSON'S OWL. *Crýptoglaux funérea ríchardsoni.*

GRAYISH BROWN

L. 9-12; W. 6.5-7.5. Upper parts reddish-brown spotted with white; under parts pale buff, striped with reddish-brown; primaries and tail barred; eyes yellow. The back of young birds is sooty-brown.

It seems to see so poorly in day light as to be almost blind, so that one may sometimes catch them in his hands.

They nest in hollow trees or in the branches and lay 2 to 7 plain white eggs. Owl eggs are much more nearly spherical than the eggs of most birds.

Figure 100

11b Smaller; with dark face; forehead finely streaked with white. Fig. 101.

372 SAW-WHET OWL. *Crýptoglaux acádica acádica.*

L. 8; W. 5.4. Cinnamon brown above; head with fine streaks in front, coarser behind; shoulders and bars on primaries and tail white; under parts white with heavy cinnamon brown bars, heaviest at throat; feet feathered, white.

Its name refers to its call which seems to resemble the sound made by filing a saw.

372

Figure 101

12a White with dark spots or bars more or less in evidence; reaches our areas only in winter. Fig. 102.

376 SNOWY OWL. *Nýctea nýctea.*

WHITE

BARS PALE SLATY-BROWN

376

L. 25; W. 17. ♂ Pure white, sometimes with scarcely any color marking but more often with transverse spots or bars of slaty-brown; bill and claws black; iris lemon yellow. ♀ Darker than male, the face, throat, chest and feet only, being pure white; otherwise rather heavily barred with dark brownish-slate. Breeds in the Arctic or near Arctic regions and entering the mapped area rather erratically in winter.

Figure 102

47

14a Lower breast and belly with longitudinal stripes; throat with many fine cross-bars. Fig. 103.

368 NORTHERN BARRED OWL. Stríx vária vária.

L. 20; W. 13.5. Upper parts brown, barred with buff or white; tail with 6-8 narrow bands; under parts whitish marked with brown; bill yellow.

368a FLORIDA BARRED OWL. S. v. álleni. Smaller with toes almost wholly naked.

368b TEXAS BARRED OWL. S. v. helvéola. Lighter than 368; toes without feathers.

Figure 103

14b Head, and neck spotted with white; almost entire underparts dark spotted. Fig. 104.

369 CALIFORNIA SPOTTED OWL. Stríx occidentális occidentális.

L. 19; W. 13. Sepia brown above with many white spots; tail barred with lighter brown; under parts whitish or buffy with spots or short bars of brown.

369a NORTHERN SPOTTED OWL. S. o. caurína. Darker than the above with light marks smaller.

369b MEXICAN SPOTTED OWL. S. o. lúçida. The lightest colored of the three.

Figure 104

15a Entire under parts barred, face white with black border; head small, tail long and rounded. Fig. 105.

377a AMERICAN HAWK OWL. Súrnia úlula cáparoch.

L. 15; W. 9; T. 7.2. Dark brown above becoming blackish on head and neck; forehead with many small round white spots. Under parts white barred with fuscous.

This is a diurnal owl doing its hunting by day. It has many of the mannerisms of the Sparrow Hawk.

Figure 105

48

15b Breast with long broad streaks; facial disks gray with concentric circular bars of black. Fig. 106.

370 GREAT GRAY OWL. *Scotiáptex nebulósa nebulósa.*

L. 27; W. 17.5. Fuscous above, much specked and mottled with white; under parts white, the breast striped and the belly barred with fuscous; legs and feet heavily feathered; bill yellow.

This great bird breeds mostly in the far north but reaches the mapped area in winter.

Figure 106

NIGHTHAWKS, WHIP-POOR-WILLS, ETC.
Order *Caprimulgiformes*

1a Wing (both above and below) with prominent white patch. 4

1b Wing without patch of white. 2

2a A large brownish-gray bird with narrow white or buff band in throat; calls its name from resting place. Fig. 107.

416 CHUCK-WILL'S-WIDOW. *Antróstomum carolinénsis.*

L. 12; W. 8.5. Call, an instantly recognizable, much repeated "Chuck-will's-widow" with the "wid" strongly accented. Mouth bristles with hair-like branches at base. ♂ Inner vane of terminal half of outer tail feathers white. ♀ No white in tail, throat patch buff.

All the Goatsuckers are nocturnal and catch their food (mostly insects) as they fly. By day they sit lengthwise on limbs of trees or on the ground.

Figure 107

The Chuck-will's-widow has a very large mouth; small birds have been found in its stomach.

49

2b Not as in 2a. 3

3a Calls its name at night. A mottled dark brown bird. Fig. 108.
   417 EASTERN WHIP-POOR-WILL. *Antrostomus vociferus vociferus.*

L. 10; W. 6. Call, a loud rapid many times repeated "whip-poor-will" with the accent on the "will". Mouth bristles without branches. ♂ Outer tail feathers tipped with white; throat crescent, white. ♀ Throat crescent and tips of outer tail feathers buff.

Figure 108

417a STEPHEN'S WHIP-POOR-WILL. *A. v. arizónae.* Slightly larger than 417. The throat patch of ♂ is rusty instead of white.

The Whip-poor-will builds no nest but lays its brown spotted eggs directly on the dry leaves of the forest floor. One almost steps on the closely camouflaged bird before it flies from its eggs and he needs to mark the spot if he hopes to find it again.

3b Call "Poor-will". White or buff tips of outer tail feathers narrower than in 3a. Fig. 109.
   418 NUTTALL'S POOR-WILL. *Phalaenóptilus núttalli núttalli.*

L. 8. Call (night) a lound many-times repeated "Poor-will". ♂ Throat patch large, white; tail with narrow even tip of white; primaries rusty with bars of black. ♀ With buff tail tip.

418b DUSKY POOR-WILL. *P. n. califórnicus.* Somewhat darker.

Figure 109

418c The DESERT POOR-WILL. *P. n. húeyni.* Lighter colored. It is found in desert areas of our Southwest.

The Poor-will lays two spotless white eggs on bare ground. It shows little inclination to move when approached during the day but lives an active life at night.

4a White patch on wing about midway between bend and tip. Flies high. Fig. 110.

420 EASTERN NIGHTHAWK. *Chordeíles mínor mínor.*

Figure 110

L. 10; W. 7.8. Call (in flight) a single nasal "peent". ♂ Upper parts mottled black, white and buff; tail blackish with narrow white band near tip (not crossing two middle feathers). Large white throat patch. ♀ Throat patch dark buff, no white on tail.

420a WESTERN NIGHTHAWK. C. m. hénryi. More yellowish and browner.

420b FLORIDA NIGHTHAWK. C. m. chápmani. Smaller than 420.

420c SENNETT'S NIGHTHAWK. C. m. sennetti. Very light colored.

420d PACIFIC NIGHTHAWK. C. m. hésperis. Lighter than 420.

420e HOWELL'S NIGHTHAWK. C. m. hówelli. Browner than 420c.

420f CHERRIE'S NIGHTHAWK. C. m. aserriénsis. Colored like 420c but much smaller.

Flying nighthawks are a familiar sight in any city in early evenings. The grayish speckeled eggs are laid and incubated on the gravel roofs of flat topped buildings, or in the country on flat rocks or on bare ground.

4b Smaller and browner, low flying bird with white bar much closer to tip than bend of wing. Fig. 111.

421 TEXAS NIGHTHAWK. *Chordeíles acutipénnis texénsis.*

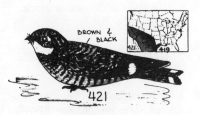

Figure 111

L. 8.5; Mottled black and white with numerous rusty spots on wings and under parts. First primary shorter than second. Flies low over the ground. Call a very peculiar humming or mewing sound.

419 MERRILL'S PAURAQUE. Nyc-tídromus albicóllis mérrilli. (L. 12) Comes north to southern Texas. General color gray or rusty. Outer tail feather ♂ black, ♀ brown, next two, partly white. Its whistled night call has been interpreted as a repeated "ker-whe-eeer".

51

SWIFTS Family *Micropodidae*

1a Tail without spines; at least somewhat forked. 2

1b Tail very short and stubby, with protruding spines. Fig. 112.

Figure 112

423 CHIMNEY SWIFT. *Chaetúra pelágica.* L. 5.4; W. 5. Above sooty-olive to grayish-brown, under parts somewhat lighter, especially the throat which is occasionally almost grayish-white.

424 VAUX'S SWIFT. *C. vaúxi.* L. 4.5; W. 4.4. Noticeably smaller and with rump, upper tail coverts and especially the under parts paler than 423.

Hollow trees once served for nesting sites and general headquarters. When civilization came along, chimney's were put to use by these birds. Their "bow and arrow" shape as they skim through the skies for food or pleasure is readily recognized. They are not "swallows".

2a Distinctly marked with white. Fig. 113.

    425 WHITE-THROATED SWIFT. *Aëronaútes saxátalis saxátalis.*

Figure 113

L. 6; W. 5.7. Grayish-brown to dark sooty brown. Each side of rump, tips of outer web of secondaries and parts of throat, breast and abdomen white (or often tinged with brownish) as pictured.

It flies very swiftly in an erratic pattern. The nest is inaccessible on cañon walls of high promontories.

2b Sooty-black without white markings. Fig. 114.

    422 BLACK SWIFT. *Nephoécetes níger boreális.*

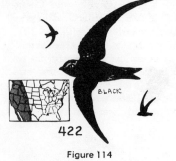

Figure 114

L. 7; W. 6.5. Paler below. Feathers on under parts of female white tipped. Tail of ♀ square, of ♂ somewhat notched.

The nest is built on the sides of steep high cliffs or occasionally on the cornice of a building.

52

HUMMINGBIRDS
Family *Trochilidae*

These very interesting fellows have a metallic sheen to most of their colors and are often highly iridescent. It should be understood that their apparent color shades vary with the lighting and angle of vision.

1a Throat and sometimes the crown covered with a brightly colored *gorget* (a metalic like ornament of specialized feathers). Tail (except in #427) narrow and without any white at tip. MALES 2

1b Throat without gorget. Tail broad, rounded and with more or less conspicuous white spots at tip. FEMALES. 16

MALES

2a Red on throat. 3

2b With no red on throat. 8

3a Upper parts and sides some shade of metallic green. 5

3b At least the tail-coverts and tail, of upper parts, and the sides red brown. 4

4a Back greenish, tail and sides rufous. Fig. 115.
434 ALLEN'S HUMMINGBIRD. *Selásphorus álleni.*

Figure 115

L. 3.4; W. 1.5. ♂ Back bronze-green; upper tail-coverts and tail dark rufous; chin and throat metallic scarlet; bill dull black. ♀ Back and apical half of tail green with shades of rufous midway; outer tail feathers tipped with white; sides light rufous; throat white often with small spots of orange-red.

4b Upper parts and sides rufous. Fig. 116.
433 RUFOUS HUMMINGBIRD. *Selásphorus rúfus.*

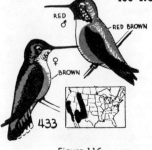

Figure 116

L. 3.4; W. 1.6. ♂ Upper parts bright rufous (back sometimes with sheen of green-bronze). Chest white, sides rufous; throat metallic scarlet; bill dull black. ♀ Upper parts bronze-green; base of tail rufous; tips of outer tail feathers white; throat and chest dull white, the throat often specked with orange-red.

5a Head with no red on top. **6**

5b Head with red on top. Fig. 117.

431 ANNA'S HUMMINGBIRD. *Calýpte ánna.*

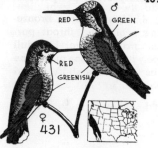

Figure 117

L. 4; W. 2. ♂ Entire head except occiput metallic rose-red. Upper parts and sides bronze-green; chest dull grayish-white; bill dull black. ♀ Top of head and other upper parts bronze-green; tail broad, rounded, outer feathers tipped with white; throat and chest dull grayish-white, the chin and throat sometimes with a metallic red spot.

6a Throat gorget solid red. **7**

6b Throat with red rays on a background of white; very small. Fig. 118.

436 CALLIOPE HUMMINGBIRD. *Stéllula callíope.*

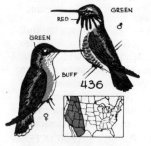

Figure 118

L. 3 (or less); W. 1.6. ♂ Upper parts bronze-green. Throat and chest white, but thinly covered with the elongated, narrow red feathers of the "gorget"; bill mostly dark. ♀ Usually showing more · bronze above than the male; chin, and throat brownish-white, often streaked or specked with brown; sides buff; tail-feathers tipped with white.

7a Tail forked; breast and sides greenish-brown; eastern. Fig. 119.

428 RUBY-THROATED HUMMINGBIRD. *Archílochus cólubris.*

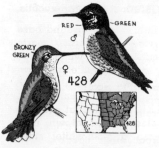

Figure 119

L. 3.3; W. 1.6. ♂ Upper parts bronze-green; tail bronzed purplish-black; area at base of bill velvety black; throat geranium-red, highly iridescent; chest dull brownish-white above becoming dark brownish gray below; bill dull black. ♀ Upper parts bronze to golden green; tail double rounded, the feathers with prominent white tips.

This is the only Hummingbird regularly found in the central and eastern United States and Canada.

7b Tail rounded; breast pale gray; sides gray overlaid with green; western. Fig. 120.

432 BROAD-TAILED HUMMINGBIRD. *Selásphorus platycércus platycércus.*

L. 3.6; W. 2. ♂ Upper parts bronze-green, tail dark; chin and throat purplish-red; chest grayish-white; bill dull black. ♀ Upper parts bronze-green the tail rounded, its feathers broadly tipped with white.

The nest of a hummingbird is a work of art.

Figure 120

8a Throat with purple. 13

8b Throat green or blue. 9

9a With one or two prominent white lines near eye. 10

9b At most only a white dot on side of face, no prominent lines....11

10a Outer tail feathers heavily tipped with white; throat blue. Large.
Fig. 121.   **427a TEXAS BLUE-THROATED HUMMINGBIRD.**
Lampórnis cleménciae clémenciae.

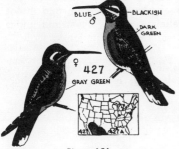

L. 4.8; W. 3.1. ♂ Upper parts dull bronze-green; tail black the outer feathers broadly tipped with white; throat metallic blue, sometimes with a greenish or purplish sheen; bill dull black. ♀ Similar to male except throat is the same dull brownish-gray of the entire underparts.

427 · ARIZONA BLUE-THROATED HUMMINGBIRD. *L. c. bessóphilus.* Very similar to the preceeding subspecies. No field distinctions.

Figure 121

10b No white on tail; forehead and chin purple. Fig. 122.
440.1 WHITE-EARED HUMMINGBIRD. *Hylocháris leucótis leucótis.*

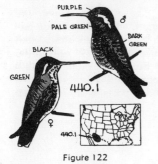

L. 3.6; W. 2.2. ♂ Entire region around base of bill violet or violet-blue; upper parts green to blackish; a broad white stripe back of eye as pictured; middle and lower throat emerald green; bill coral red. ♀ Similar to male but lacking the purple and green of head and throat. Throat grayish-white, striped or flecked with brown; mid-chest and abdomen grayish-white; sides bronze-green; bill darker.

Figure 122

11a No purple in crown. 12

11b Crown purple; throat bright green; under parts black. Fig. 123.
426 RIVOLI'S HUMMINGBIRD. *Eúgenes fúlgens.*

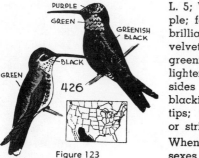

L. 5; W. 2.9. Crown violet or royal purple; forehead blackish; chin and throat brilliant metallic emerald green; chest velvety black; upper parts blackish with greenish sheen; bill dull black. ♀ Much lighter colored; top of head, back and sides metallic green; tail and wings blackish; outer tail feathers with white tips; throat dull grayish-white flecked or striped with greenish.

When at rest the wing tips of both sexes extend beyond the tail, a good distinguishing character.

Figure 123

12a Breast buff, throat green. Fig. 124.
439 BUFF-BELLIED HUMMINGBIRD. *Amazília yucatanénsis chalconóta.*

L. 4; W. 2.2. ♂ Above bronze green, the tail and upper tail-coverts brownish; chin and throat bright metallic yellowish-green; chest and under parts buff; bill coral red. ♀ Similar to male.

438 RIEFFER'S HUMMINGBIRD. *A. tzacatl tzacatl.* Abdomen brownish gray; lores chestnut; otherwise much like the above.

These two species are substantially the same in size and range.

Figure 124

12b Breast bronze-green; throat blue; bill red. Fig. 125.
441 BROAD-BILLED HUMMINGBIRD. *Cynánthus latiróstris.*

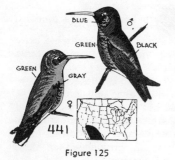

L. 3.7; W. 2. Above bronze-green; tail and wings darker; chin and throat metallic greenish-blue; breast sides and abdomen bronze-green; bill red, darkened at tip; ♀ Similar to male but duller in color; outer tail feathers tipped with white; under parts sooty-gray; bill darker.

Figure 125

56

13a White line back of eye; middle and lower throat pale green; bill red. See Fig. 122.   **WHITE-EARED HUMMINGBIRD.**

13b Without white line back of eye; bill black. 14

14a Crown not purple. ....15 .

14b Crown and throat both purple. Fig. 126.
     430 COSTA'S HUMMINGBIRD. *Calýpte cóstae.*

L. 3.3; W. 1.8. ♂ Head including throat, brilliant metallic violet or purple, highly iridescent; rest of upper parts bronze-green; chest and midbreast grayish-white; sides greenish-gray; bill dull black. ♀ Dull bronze-green above, often grayish on top of head, wings darker; chin and throat whitish; breast pale brownish-gray.

Figure 126

15a Chin and upper throat velvety black; bill straight. Fig. 127.
  429 BLACK-CHINNED HUMMINGBIRD. *Archílochus alexándri.*

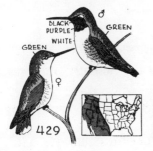

L. 3.4; W. 1.7. ♂ Dull bronze-green above, darker on crown; chin, face and upper throat velvety black; lower throat metallic violet or purple, appearing black at some angles; chest and under parts dull grayish white; sides greenish; bill dull black. ♀ Above dull bronze-green; the crown usually lighter; outer tail-feathers tipped with white; under parts dull white, the throat often with dusky or streaks or spots.

Figure 127

15b Chin and throat wholly purple; sides rusty; bill curved downward. Fig. 128.

  437 LUCIFER HUMMINGBIRD. *Calothórax lúcifer.*

L. 3.6; W. 1.5. ♂ Bronze-green or golden green above; tail and wings darker; chin and throat brilliant magenta purple or violet, the posterior feathers of gorget much elongated; chest dull white; sides light cinnamon; bill dull black, curved downward. ♀ Colored above much as in male; areas of buff and gray on side of head; under parts buff to dull whitish.

Figure 128

KEY TO THE FEMALE HUMMINGBIRDS

Some of the females cannot be accurately determined to species except by their association with their more definitely marked mates. We are not promising much for this key to the females but hope it may give some little help.

16a Sides buff or tawny. 22

16b Sides not buff or tawny. 17

17a Throat, breast and sides uniformly brownish or sooty-gray.....18

17b Throat and usually the breast light (with or without streaks or specks). 19

18a Bill dull black; much white on tail, length 4.8 inches. BLUE-THROATED HUMMINGBIRDS. Fig. 121.

18b Bill reddish; but little white on tail; length 3.7 inches. BROAD-BILLED HUMMINGBIRD. Fig. 125.

19a Sides whitish. BLACK-CHINNED HUMMINGBIRD. Fig. 127 or COSTA'S HUMMINGBIRD. Fig. 126. (closely similar) THE RUBY-THROATED HUMMINGBIRD. Fig. 119, ranging in the East could fall here also.

19b Sides greenish. 20

20a Bill black. 21

20b Bill in part reddish. WHITE-EARED HUMMINGBIRD. Fig. 122.

21a Wings when at rest extending beyond tail. RIVOLI'S HUMMING-BIRD. Fig. 123.

21b Wings not extending beyond tail, often small red spot or spots in throat. ANNA'S HUMMINGBIRD. Fig. 117.

22a Bill in part reddish. BUFF-BELLIED HUMMINGBIRD. Fig. 124.

22b Bill black. 23

23a Bill curved downward. LUCIFER'S HUMMINGBIRD. Fig. 128.

23b Bill straight. 24

24a Inhabits Eastern United States and Canada. RUBY-THROATED HUMMINGBIRD. Fig. 119.

24b Found only in the West. 25

25a Rump altogether rusty. ALLEN'S HUMMINGBIRD. Fig. 115. RUFOUS HUMMINGBIRD. Fig. 116. (closely similar).

25b Rump green at middle. CALLIOPE HUMMINGBIRD. L. 3 in. Fig. 118. BROAD-TAILED HUMMINGBIRD. L. 3.6 in. Fig. 120. (closely similar except for size).

KINGFISHERS
Order *Coraciiformes*

1a Bluish gray above; larger. Fig. 129.
   390 EASTERN BELTED KINGFISHER. *Megacéryle álcyon álcyon.*

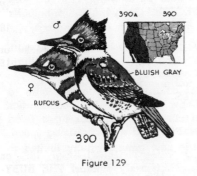

Figure 129

L. 13; W. 6.3. ♀ With gray band on upper breast and narrow chestnut band below, widening into a broad longitudinal stripe at either side. ♂ Similar to female but without the chestnut markings.

390a WESTERN BELTED KINGFISHER. *C. a caurína.* Somewhat larger. These birds nest in long horizontal tunnels in the side of a bank. Six glossy white eggs are usually laid. Insects, crayfish and frogs supplement their diet of fish. Their rattling call is easily recognized.

1b Greenish above; smaller. Fig. 130.
   391 TEXAS KINGFISHER. *Chlorocéryle americána septentrionális.*

Figure 130

L. 7.5; W. 3.5. ♂ Breast with broad rusty brown band, and white collar entirely around the neck. ♀ With white breast and throat often tinged with buff; a band of greenish spots crosses the lower breast.

Like the Belted Kingfisher, this very much smaller bird lays claim to the fishing rights on a definite piece of creek or other water-place and boldly defends it. It often fishes from a rock or sand-bar.

WOODPECKERS
Order *Piciformes*

1a Large bird with prominent crest. 2

1b Without a crest. 3

2a Bill ivory white; large white patch near tip of wing. Fig. 131.
     392 IVORY-BILLED WOODPECKER. *Campéphilus principális.*

Figure 131

L. 20; W. 10. Shining black marked with white as pictured. ♂ With very brilliant red crest. Crest of ♀ black.

This great colorful bird (larger than a crow) is now very rare. Its food consists mostly of insects. It can tear up a dead log in quest for food with surprising speed. Its range is now almost wholly limited to the deep forest swamp lands of Louisiana and Florida. The chances for seeing one are not at all favorable.

2b Bill dark. Fig. 132.

Figure 132

405 SOUTHERN PILEATED WOODPECKER.
Ceophloéus pileátus pileátus.

L. 17; W. 8.9. Black tinged with slate or brownish and marked with white as pictured. Base of wing feathers white, showing considerable white when in flight but scantily revealed when at rest. ♂ Entire top of head and a narrow stripe below the eye, scarlet. ♀ Front of crown brownish-black; no red stripe under eye.

405a NORTHERN PILEATED WOODPECKER. *C. p. abietícola.* A larger bird with longer bill and the black more slate tinged.

405b FLORIDA PILEATED WOODPECKER. *C. p. floridánus.* A better black than #405, smaller and with shorter and heavier bill.

405c WESTERN PILEATED WOODPECKER. *C. p. picínus.* Larger and considerably darker than 405.

3a Head not white. **4**

3b Head white, with or without red nape band. Fig. 133.

399 NORTHERN WHITE-HEADED WOODPECKER.
Dryóbates albolarvátus albolarvátus.

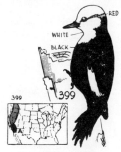

Figure 133

L. 9; W. 5. Black, somewhat glossy except wings which are dull. Head and patch on wing as pictured, white. ♂ With poppy red nape band. ♀ Without red band.

399a THE SOUTHERN WHITE-HEADED WOODPECKER. *D. a. graviróstris.* Similar but with a noticably larger bill.

4a Head wholly red. **5**

4b Head but partly or not at all red. **6**

5a Belly, rump, upper tail-coverts and secondaries white. Fig. 134.

406 RED-HEADED WOODPECKER. *Melanérpes erythrocéphalus.*

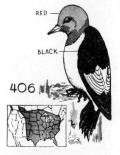

Figure 134

L. 9; W. 5.5. Head, neck and upper breast bright crimson (chocolate brown in young birds). Back, scapulars, primaries and tail black, in part with bluish iridescence; other parts white as pictured.

This interesting bird has a habit of taking his insect catches to some hard surface where he pounds them up. Our cement highways, seem just the spot, but like other juvenile minds, he's slow to learn that it is a most hazardous place to play.

5b Belly yellowish; back black with longitudinal white markings. Fig. 135.

403 SOUTHERN RED-BREASTED SAPSUCKER.
Sphyrápicus várius dággetti.

Figure 135

L. 8.5; W. 5. Head, neck and breast red (bright in spring; becoming dull later). Back wings and tail black with white markings, belly yellowish. Young birds with duller colors.

403a NORTHERN RED-BREASTED SAPSUCKER. *S. v. rúber.* Averages a bit larger with the red and yellow markings brighter.

6a Main back color brown. 7

6b Main back color not brown. 10

7a Wings and back with transverse rows of black spots, rump white. Fairly large birds. 8

7b Wings and back rather plain brown obscurely marked with white. Rump brown. Smaller than 7a. Fig. 136.
    398 ARIZONA WOODPECKER. *Dryóbates arizónae arizónae.*

L. 8; W. 4.6. Head marked with streaks of brown and white. Male with nape red; no red on female. Back and wings in varying shades of brown, tail darker. Under parts whitish, thickly spotted with dark brown.

Young birds are unusual in having red crowns.

Figure 136

8a Without red on nape. (if the head and neck are wholly brown with cross bars on flank see the ♀ of # 404 Fig. 144.). 9

8b With red crescent on nape. Fig. 137.
    412a NORTHERN FLICKER. *Coláptes aurátus lúteus.*

L. 13; W. 6.4. Head, face and neck light grayish-brown. Back and wings brown with crossbars of black; tail black above, golden yellow with black markings beneath. Rump white. Lower chest black; other under parts buff with black dots. Under wings brilliant golden yellow. ♂ with black whisker mark under eye. ♀ without whisker mark.

412 SOUTHERN FLICKER. *C. a. auratus.* Similar but smaller. Alabama has made it their state bird.

When you see a Flicker busily digging into the ground you may know he's lunching on ants. Ants make up much of their food.

Figure 137

9a Wings and tail lined with salmon-red. Fig. 138.
413 RED-SHAFTED FLICKER. *Coláptes cáfer colláris.*

Figure 138

L. 13; W. 6.8. Marked and colored much as 412a except for characters in key. The shafts of the primaries give a reddish tinge to that part of the wing. The nape has no red in either sex but the ♂ has a red whisker mark which is wanting in the ♀.

9b Lining of wings and tail golden yellow. Fig. 139.
414a MEARN'S GILDED FLICKER. *Coláptes chrysóides meárnsi.*

Figure 139

L. 12; W. 6. This desert flicker has a head marked the same as the Red-shafted Flicker but the yellow wing and tail lining of the Northern Flicker. The sexes may be distinguished by the red whisker mark in the ♂ and its absence in the ♀. Neither sex has a nape band of red.

10a Smaller northern woodpeckers with much depressed bill, only three toes, and yellow (♂) or black (♀) crest. 11

10b Not as in 10a. 12

11a Back wholly black. Fig. 140.
400 ARCTIC THREE-TOED WOODPECKER. *Picoídes árcticus.*

Figure 140

L. 9.5; W. 5.4. Back black with bluish tinge; under parts white; crown of ♂ bright canary yellow to orange. ♀ plain black. Two toes forward; one back.

This little woodpecker is quite unafraid and also quite rare. It seems to be largely restricted to burned over areas of spruce and balsam.

11b Back and flanks with prominent cross-bars of white. Fig. 141.

401 AMERICAN THREE-TOED WOODPECKER.
Picoïdes tridáctylus bacátus.

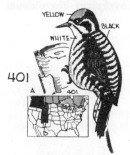

L. 9; W. 4.6. Black marked with white as pictured. ♂ with pale yellow crown; ♀ with crown black, sometimes specked with white.

401a ALASKA THREE-TOED WOODPECKER. *P. t. fasciátus.* A little larger than the preceeding, with more white on the back and forehead.

401b ALPINE THREE-TOED WOODPECKER. *P. t. dorsális.* Has much white on the back, the area usually having no black cross bars. It is still larger than 401a.

Figure 141

12a. Wings, back and tail shining green-black; belly pinkish-red. Fig. 142. **408 LEWIS'S WOODPECKER.** *Asyndésmus léwis.*

L. 11; W. 7. Crown, nape, back, wings and tail black, tinged with metallic iridescence.

Forehead and face as pictured, dark crimson; a broad collar light silvery-gray; under parts pinkish-red. These markings and colors are practically the same in both sexes. Young birds do not have the red markings.

This bird was discovered by the Lewis and Clark expedition, hence the name.

Figure 142

12b Not as in 12a. **13**
13a Belly yellow or yellowish. **14**
13b Belly not marked with yellow. **16**
14a With prominent white patch on black wing. **15**
14b Back with black and white fine cross-bars. Fig. 143.

410 GOLDEN-FRONTED WOODPECKER. *Centúrus aúrifrons.*

L. 10.5; W. 5.5. ♂ Forehead bright yellow; crown, poppy-red; nape orange. Rest of head and breast pale grayish-buff; center of belly yellow. ♀ Forehead and nape yellow, crown wholly grayish-buff.

411 GILA WOODPECKER. *C. uropygiális uropygialis.* Similar. The ♂ has only the red crown with forehead and nape sooty-gray ♀ Head wholly sooty-gray.

The ♀ of #404 with plain brown head (Fig. 144) might be confused with these.

Figure 143

15a B:ck wholly black (finely barred in ♀). No red on crown. Fig. 144.
  404 WILLIAMSON'S SAPSUCKER. *Sphyrápicus thyroídeus.*

Figure 144

L. 9; W. 5.5. ♂ Head black with white mark-ings; chin and upper throat bright red; belly bright yellow; rump white. ♀ Crown and throat brownísh; back with cross-bars of black on brownish-white or pale drab; middle tail feath-ers barred with white.

This is our only male American four-toed wood-pecker that is not marked in some way with red on the head. The female was for a period of years considered a separate species and was known as the Brown-headed Woodpecker.

15b Crown red. Fig. 145.
  402 YELLOW-BELLIED SAPSUCKER. *Sphyrápicus várius várius.*

Figure 145

L. 8.5; W. 4.8. ♂ Forehead, crown, chin and throat red; nape white; under parts pale yellow. ♀ Throat and chin white. (Crown rarely black instead of red.).

402a RED-NAPED SAPSUCKER. *S. v. nuch-alis.* Similar to 402 but with less white on the back. Nape red with crescent of black separating it from red crown. ♀ Chin white; throat wholly red or upper part white.

Questions are often asked about the hori-zontal rows of round holes frequently seen in the bark of trees. The sapsuckers make them in the spring and drink the sweet sap that collects in the holes. Insects at-tracted to the sap are also eaten by these birds.

16a Nape and center of belly red. Fig. 146.
409 RED-BELLIED WOODPECKER. *Centúrus carolínus.*

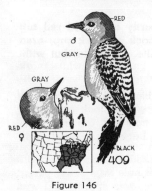

Figure 146

L. 9.5; W. 5.3. ♂ General color light gray; forehead crown and nape poppy-red; back and wings with rather fine black and white cross-bars. ♀ Crown gray, nape red; forehead sometimes tinged with red; red spot on belly usually smaller.

This bird has a habit of eating fruit, usually wild species but sometimes doing damage in orchards.

16b Not as in 16a. 17

17a Throat yellow with small red spot beneath it; crown and nape red; back black. Fig. 147.
407 ANT-EATING WOODPECKER. *Balanosphýra formicívora.*

Figure 147

L. 9.5; W. 5.6. ♂ Chin and upper throat black, lower throat yellow or yellowish-white; crown and nape bright red; wings, back, tail and under parts black and white as pictured. ♀ Crown black.

407a CALIFORNIA WOODPECKER. *B. f. baîrdi.* Largest of the three subspecies and with darker yellow on throat and more black on the breast.

407c MEARN'S WOODPECKER. *B. f. aculeáta.* Somewhat smaller and with considerable black on breast.

17b Black and white birds with or without red on the head........18

18a Back with fine cross-bars of black and white; under parts whitish with streaks or spots of black on flanks. 19

18b Under parts whitish without streaks or spots, back white. 21

19a Cap of male, red; of female, black; western. 20

66

19b Cap black: south-eastern. Fig. 148.

395 RED-COCKADED WOODPECKER. *Dryóbates boreális.*

L. 8; W. 4.5. ♂ With a partly concealed red tuft on each side of head at back of black cap; area back of and below eye white. ♀ Similar but without red on head.

It frequents pine woods.

If tempted to confuse this bird with the Downy as is sometimes done, compare the black and white markings of the back and note that the red markings do not run across the back of the head as in the Downy.

Figure 148

20a Forehead black. Fig. 149.

397 NUTTALL'S WOODPECKER. *Dryóbates núttalli.*

L. 7.5; W. 4. ♂ Much of crown black often streaked with white; back of crown and nape bright red; lower neck behind and upper back black; outer tail feathers white except for one or two black spots near tip. ♀ No red on head, black instead.

The 4 to 6 white eggs are laid in holes in dead limbs not far from the ground. The food consists mostly of insects.

Figure 149

20b Forehead brownish. Fig. 150.

396 TEXAS WOODPECKER. *Dryóbates scaláris sympléctus.*

L. 7.5; W. 4. ♂ Crown and nape red; neck behind and back with black cross-bars; outer tail feathers white with several black bars. ♀ Red of male replaced with black.

396b CACTUS WOODPECKER. *D. s. cactóphilus.* A bit larger than 396 with black bars wider.

These birds live in arid regions. Several other subspecies are found throughout much of Mexico.

Figure 150

21a Outer tail feathers white or whitish without bars; larger birds with strong bill; wing usually over 4½ inches. Fig. 151.
393 EASTERN HAIRY WOODPECKER. *Dryóbates villósus villósus.*

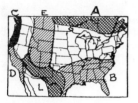

L. 9; W. 4.8. Sharply contrasting black and white as pictured. ♂ Red band on nape. ♀ Closely similar but with white nape band.

393a NORTHERN HAIRY WOODPECKER. *D. v. septentrionális.* Definitely larger than 393 with larger and clearer white markings.

393b SOUTHERN HAIRY WOODPECKER. *D. v. aúduboni.* Noticeably smaller than 393. (The smallest of the subspecies listed here.)

393c HARRIS'S WOODPECKER. *D. v. hárrisi.* Under parts light drab. Somewhat larger than 393.

393d CABANIS'S WOODPECKER. *D. v. hylóscopus.* About the size of 393. Under parts dull grayish.

393

Figure 151

393e ROCKY MOUNTAIN HAIRY WOOD-PECKER. *D. v. montícola.* Largest of the Hairies. Under parts clean white; white spots on wing-coverts, smaller.

393h CHIHUAHUA WOODPECKER. *D. v. icástus.* A bit larger than 393, under parts dull.

393j MODOC WOODPECKER. *D. v. órius.* Fairly large but smaller than 393e; under parts with grayish tinge.

393l WHITE-BREASTED WOODPECKER. *D. v. leucothoréctis.* Colored like 393e but smaller.

21b White tail feathers with black bars (sometimes indistinct in 394d.) Smaller birds with small bills; wing usually less than 4 inches. Fig. 152.

394 SOUTHERN DOWNY WOODPECKER. *Dryóbates pubéscens.*

L. 6; W. 3.5. Black and white. ♂ With red nape band. ♀ Nape white.

394a GAIRDNER'S WOODPECKER. *D. p. gaírdneri.* Larger than 394. White parts tinged with brownish-gray.

394b BATCHELDER'S WOODPECKER. *D. p. leucúrus.* The largest Downy. White on wing-coverts reduced or even wanting.

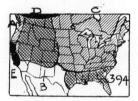

Figure 152

394c NORTHERN DOWNY WOODPECK-ER. *D. p. mediánus.* Larger than 394 and the white less grayed.

394d NELSON'S DOWNY WOODPECKER. *D. p. nélsoni.* Larger than 394c. The white cleanly cut; bars on outer tail feathers less evident.

394e WILLOW WOODPECKER. *D. p. turáti.* Considerably smaller than 394b; under parts grayish.

PERCHING BIRDS
Order *Passeriformes*

1a Bill cone-shaped. (Fig. 153). 2

1b Not definitely cone-shaped for seed eating.

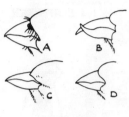

Figure 153

2a Bill short and heavy for crushing seeds, etc.; first primary, only a little shorter than 3rd. and 4th. with bristles usually present. Some shade of brown often the predominating color (sparrows) but others brilliantly colored. Fig. 153. 3

2b Bills slimmer. 4

3a Altogether too well-known introduced sparrows (as pictured and described). Fig. 154.
EUROPEAN HOUSE SPARROWS, Family *Ploceidae*.
688.2 ENGLISH SPARROW. *Passer domésticus domésticus.*

688.2

Figure 154

L. 6.4; W. 3. ♂ Crown gray prominently marked on neck and back with reddish-brown; wing-coverts reddish-brown with a white wingbar; tl .oat and breast black; belly and sides of throat light gray. ♀ Upper parts gray, streaked with buff and blackish; under parts light tinged with brown on sides. Now scattered almost world-wide.

688.3 EUROPEAN TREE SPARROW. *Passer montánus montánus.*

Both sexes with black spot in throat similar to the ♂ English Sparrow but with black spot back of eye also. It has been introduced into parts of Missouri and possibly elsewhere.

It should be noted that these two birds belong to a different family from our native Sparrows, keyed and described later.

3b Native birds not as in 3a. FINCHES, GROSSBEAKS, SPARROWS AND BUNTINGS. Family *Fringillidae*. . . . . .page 150

4a With prominent bristles over nostrils and at base of bill; claw of hind toe much elongated; feathers of head forming two horn-like structures. Birds of the roadside and open fields, where they scratch in the loose ground. Fig. 155. LARKS, Family *Alaudidae*.

474 NORTHERN HORNED LARK. *Otócoris alpéstris alpéstris*.

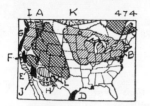

BREEDING AREAS

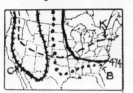

474

Figure 155

WINTER RANGE

L. 7-8; W. 4.3. ♂ Grayish-brown, with black and sulphur-yellow markings about head and throat; lower breast and belly white washed in part with blackish; tail largely black. ♀ Smaller and duller colored. Walks instead of hopping.

In all, 16 subspecies have been named. We have mapped their breeding areas and also the approximate winter range of the more abundant subspecies. There is much overlapping, especially in winter and during migration.

Four subspecies range east of the Rockies,—(474) NORTHERN; (474b) PRAIRIE; (474d) TEXAS and (474k) HOYT'S HORNED LARKS. From the Rocky Mountains west to the coast the following occur,—(474a) PALLID; (474c) DESERT; (474e) CALIFORNIA; (474f) RUDDY; (474g) STREAKED; (474h) SCORCHED; (474i) DUSKY; (474j) SONORA; (474l) MONTEZUMA; (474m) ISLAND; (474n) MAGDALENA and (474o) MOHAVA HORNED LARKS.

4b Without bristles, horns or long back claw as above; Upper bill curved with tooth at middle (A). Males in part at least red; females dull colored. Birds of the forest treetops. Fig. 156.

TANGERS, Family *Thraupidae*. page 148

Figure 156

5a Feeds on insects most of which are taken from the air as the bird flies. 6

5b Food not taken as in 5a. 7

6a Flies out and back from perching places, usually on a dead limb, to catch passing insects; fairly large bristles at base of bill, tip of bill bent downward; tail with 12 feathers; first primary not greatly shortened. Fig. 157.

THE TYRANT FLYCATCHERS, Family *Tyrannidae*. page 78

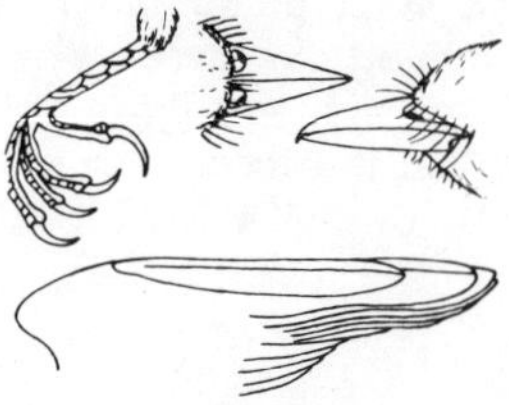

Figure 157

6b Feeding flights continued for long periods. Bill flattened, very short and without bristles; feet small; tail often deeply notched; wing with but 9 primaries. Fig. 158.

THE SWALLOWS, Family *Hirundinidae*. page 87

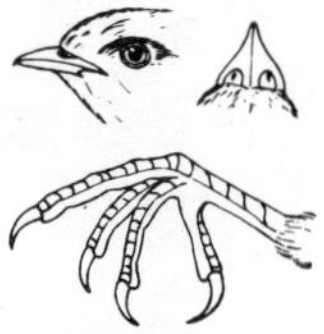

Figure 158

7a Small brownish climbing bird with long slim bill curving downward and sharp pointed tail feathers curving upward, used for prop. Fig. 159.   CREEPERS, Family *Certhiidae*.
· 726 BROWN CREEPER. *Cérthia familiáris americána.*

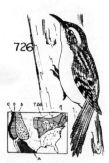

726

Figure 159

L. 5.7; W. 2.6. Upper parts brownish, mottled with reddish-white and buff; rump pale rufous; under parts white or whitish. Examines tree trunks beginning near the ground and moving upward to the first limbs or a bit higher then flying back to base and starting up again by a different route. The long tongue is used to pick out insect eggs and other food bits.

726a MEXICAN CREEPER. *C. f. albéscens.* Somewhat larger, darker and more dusky than the preceeding, with the white more pronounced.

726b ROCKY MOUNTAIN CREEPER. *C. f. montána.* Somewhat lighter colored than 726.

726c CALIFORNIA CREEPER. *C. f. occidentális.* Darker and browner above than 726a with more buff.

726d SIERRA CREEPER. *C. f. zelótes.* Similar to 726b but darker, the white more limited.

7b Not as in 7a. 8

8a Nostrils covered with hair like feathers. See Fig. 161B. 9

8b Nostrils not covered with hairs. 12

72

9a Two parts of bill about equal in size, neither bending over the other. 10

9b Upper mandible longer with hooked tip bending over the lower mandible. Principal color grayish. Fig. 160.
           SHRIKES. Family *Laniidae* page 117

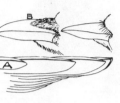

Figure 160

10a From over 10 inches long to quite large birds; bill sturdy; outer tail feathers the shortest; first primary (A) only half the length of the fourth and fifth which are longest of all. Fig. 161. CROWS, JAYS, and MAGPIES, Family *Corvidae* page 90

Figure 161

10b Not over 6 inches long. 11

11a Creeping birds often walking on trees with head downward; color slate gray with markings of black, white or brown. Tail short, not used for propping. Bill compressed, slender about as long as head. Fig. 162. NUTHATCHES, Family *Sittidae* page 100

Figure 162

11b Head about twice as long as the short rounded bill. First primary very short. Fig. 163. TITMICE, VERDINS AND BUSH-TITS. Family *Paridae* page 96

Figure 163

12a With a tall slim crest. 13

12b Without a crest. 14

13a Sleek grayish-brown; black band passing through eyes and crossing forehead; bill hooked and with small notch at tip; tip of secondaries often with bright red waxen wafers; tip of tail yellow. Fig. 164A.
     WAXWINGS, Family *Bombycillidae.* page 116

Figure 164

13b Glossy black or dark gray; tail solid color, notched. Figs. 164B
and 165. SILKY FLYCATCHERS, Family *Ptilogonatidae*.
620 PHAINOPEPLA. *Phainopépla nítens lépida*.

GREENISH

GREENISH
BLUE-BLACK

GREENISH
WHITE

620

Figure 165

L. 7.8; W. 3.6. ♂ Shining greenish-blue-
black; wings and tail plain black with
margins of gray or greenish; white patch
on primaries showing only in flight; eye,
red. ♀ Olive-drab with chest, wings and
tail darker; middle wing-coverts with white
markings; eye, brown. Feeds on flies and
fruit.

620a MEXICAN PHAINOPEPLA. *P. n. nítens.* Highly similar, ranges through Mexico and is found in western Texas.

14a Brown much barred (usually small) birds with long
sharp bills and tails often held erect. Fig. 166.
WRENS. Family *Troglodytidae* page 102

Figure 166

14b Not as in 14a. 15

15a Fairly large slim birds with medium to quite
long bill, at least somewhat curved above of-
ten very much so; bristles at base of bill.
Usually brown (slate or gray in Catbird and
Mockingbird). Fig. 167.
MOCKINGBIRDS AND THRASHERS.
Family *Mimidae* page 106

Figure 167

15b Not as in 15a. 16

16a Feathers of the forehead extending
forward on each side of the bill leav-
ing the middle exposed at the base.
Bill pointed; first three primaries about
equal; tail usually rounded at tip.
Black is the prevailing color of most
species, often with iridescent tinges
or brilliant colored areas. Fig. 168.
MEADOWLARKS, BLACKBIRDS AND
ORIOLES. Family *Icteridae* page 140

Figure 168

16b Mid-upper base of bill not between two feather extensions. 17

17a Covering of front of tarsus broken into plates (scutellate). Fig. 169A. 21

17b Covering of front of tarsus unbroken transversely ("booted"). Fig. 169B. ...18

18a Wings larger than tail. 19

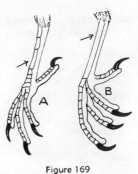

Figure 169

18b Wings shorter than tail; both tail and wings rounded. Long tailed small dusky brown wren-like birds with rather short bill. Fig. 170. WREN-TITS. Family *Chamaeidae*.

> 742 GAMBEL'S WREN-TIT. *Chamaéa fasciáta fasciáta.*

742

Figure 170

L. 6.3; W. 2.3. Brownish-olive above; underparts buffy-brown becoming darker and more drab at sides, iris of eye white.
742a PALLID WREN-TIT. *C. f. hénshawi.* A paler grayish-brown form.

742b COAST WREN-TIT. *C. f. phaéa.* This is the darkest colored of the 4 subspecies.

742c RUDDY WREN-TIT. *C. f. rúfula.* This is darker and more reddish than 742.
The distribution of these 4 subspecies so overlap each other that no attempt has been made to separate them on the map.

19a Wing over 3 inches long, breast often spotted. Figs. 250-260. ..20

19b Wing less than 2½ inches in length. Tiny olive-gray birds with or without markings of red or yellow on crown. Bill short and sharp; tail notched. See Figs. 261-262.

> KINGLETS, Family *Sylviidae.* page 114

20a With bristles on rictus (upper "lip"); for the most part brownish birds with speckled breast or with blue backs; Tail square cut; wings long and pointed with first primary (A) very short and the 3rd. the longest; tip of upper mandible notched. Fig. 171.
THRUSHES, BLUEBIRDS AND SOLITAIRES. Family *Turdidae.* page 109

Figure 171

20b **Without bristles around mouth. Rather uniformly marked slate colored bird living along mountain streams. Fig. 172.**

701 DIPPER. Cínclus mexicánus uńicolor.

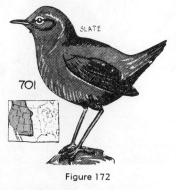

Figure 172

L. 7.5; W. 3.8. A short tailed wren-shaped bird with rather long legs. Plumage dark slate, lighter on throat and under parts; eyelids white.

Found only in the hills or mountains where swift streams provide their food, consisting largely of aquatic insects and fish eggs. They "fly" under water using their wings in swimming. The nest is placed among the rocks often in the spray of a waterfall. It is made largely of green moss. The eggs are white.

21a **Small birds less than 7 inches long.** 22

21b **Larger birds. Blackish with iridescent metallic tones; bill flattened on top and wider than high, yellow; tail square cut and short; an introduced bird, living gregariously, often in large numbers. Fig. 173. STARLINGS. Family Sturnidae.**

493 STARLING. Stúrnus vulgáris vulgáris.

L. 8.5; W. 5.1. Black when viewed from a distance. Prominently marked with metallic purplish and greenish sheens. The feathers are edged with brownish-buff which is more conspicuous in winter.

Starlings are like Dandelions, they are really beautiful and if scarce would be prized but that's the trouble. They live, feed and nest just about everywhere one would wish them not to. They imitate the calls of so many of our native birds we're always hoping to see some friend that is not there. The ill-guided-soul who planted the Starling and the English Sparrow in New York City surely played a costly joke on our country.

Figure 173

493.1 **CRESTED MYNA.** ("Japanese Starling".) *Aethiópsar cristatéllis cristatéllis.* About robin-sized; black, bill and feet light yellowish; obscure spot on wing and narrow tail tip white. The under wing coverts are white and show conspicuously in flight.
This Asiatic bird is firmly established in Vancouver, B. C. and is occasionally seen in Washington.

22a Sparrow-like but with slender bill and long hind claw; outer tail feathers white; keeps bobbing tail as it walks. Fig. 174.
PIPITS. Family *Motacillidae.*

　　　　　　697 AMERICAN PIPIT. *Ánthus spinolétta rubéscens.*

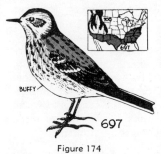

L. 6; W. 3.4. Grayish-olive or brownish; head, back and shoulders darker; buffy beneath with darker streaks; outer tail-feathers white. Found in plowed fields and other open spaces.

700 SPRAGUE'S PIPIT. *A. spráguei.* Head and back striped instead of solid color as in 697 but under parts with finer and fewer stripes.

Figure 174

22b Not as in 22a. 23

23a Tiny, slender, long-tailed gray birds with blackish markings. Fig. 114. 　　　GNATCATCHERS. Family *Sylviidae* page 114

23b Not as in 23a. 24

24a Olive-green backed birds, a bit smaller than sparrows; move deliberately among tree tops feeding on insects; bills thicker than those of the Warblers, and with the tip notched and slightly hooked. No white on tails. Fig. 175. VIREOS. Family *Vireonidae* page 118.

Figure 175

24b Very active often brightly colored birds averaging smaller than the Vireos. Bill sharp pointed; not notched at tip. First three primaries about equal. Fig. 176. WOOD WARBLERS. Family *Compsothlypidae* page 122.

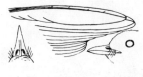

Figure 176

TYRANT FLYCATCHERS
Family *Tyrannidae*

1a With very long scissor-like tail; sides and wing linings salmon-pink. Fig. 177.

443 SCISSOR-TAILED FLYCATCHER. *Muscívora forficáta.*

Figure 177

L. 12-15; W. 5; T. 9. ♂ Upper parts pearly-gray; crown a bit darker and with a concealed spot of orange-red. Salmon to bright pink on sides and wing linings; shoulder pinkish or yellowish. Short middle tail feathers black, the long outer ones black, white and pink. ♀ Similar to male but with somewhat shorter tail.

The tail feathers are sometimes nervously opened and shut in a characteristic way.

This bird is a great "show off" or at least does a lot of fancy flying apparently just for the fun of it. The long, rather-flexible tail feathers trail gracefully in flight but on windy days seem to be a handicap. The food consists almost wholly of insects, grasshoppers constituting much of its diet. The nest, often in part or wholly of cotton is built in a bush or low tree. 4 to 6 brownish marked white eggs are laid.

1b Without tail or unusual length. 2

2a Under parts and somewhat crested head brilliant vermillion-red (♂); ♀ much plainer; under parts pale pinkish. Fig. 178.

471 VERMILION FLYCATCHER. *Pyrocéphalus rubínus mexicánus.*

Figure 178

L. 6; W. 3.2. ♂ Back, tail and wings brownish-gray to blackish; head brilliant poppy-red or scarlet, under parts a bit lighter; bill, legs and feet brownish-black. ♀ Back, wings and tail similar to male but usually lighter; malar region, throat and breast dull white, becoming pale salmon or orange farther back.

2b Not as in 2a. 3

3a With rusty brown breast; appearing like a diminutive Robin.
457 SAY'S PHOEBE. *Sayórnis sáya sáya.*

Figure 179

L. 7.5; W. 4.5. Brownish-gray above, the head and back of neck darker; upper tail-coverts grayish; tail brownish-black; chin light; under parts cinnamon buff, bill, legs and feet black. Tail with shallow notch.

It selects building ledges, etc. for its nest similar to the Eastern Phoebe.

3b Under parts not rusty-brown. 4

4a Marked in part with yellow. 8

4b Without definite yellow markings (several species falling here have light tinges of yellow). 5

5a Principally dull colored (sometimes dull tinged with yellow or olive). 13

5b Principally black and white (with or without gray parts). 6

6a Breast and sides black. Fig. 180.
458 BLACK PHOEBE. *Sayórnis nígricans nígricans.*

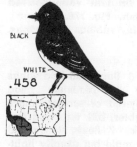

Figure 180

L. 6.5; W. 3.6. Upper parts, throat, upper breast and sides plain dark sooty-slate, the head almost black and the shoulders and rump brownish; belly and under tail-covers white.

Nests in buildings, under bridges and in caves, etc. Thought by some to be the most beautiful member of the family.

458a SAN QUINTIN PHOEBE. *S. n. salictária* gets into southern Arizona from Mexico.

6b Breast white or very light. 7

7a Tail black with white tip, square or somewhat rounded at end. Fig. 181.   444 EASTERN KINGBIRD. *Tyránnus tyránnus.*

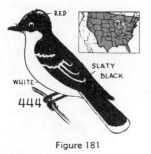

Figure 181

L. 8.5; W. 4.6. Black and gray above; white beneath; head and tail definitely black the latter with white tip and side margins; wing feathers dusky with edgings of white as pictured; under wing-coverts with much white or yellowish-white. The orange-red patch on the crown may be concealed or displayed at will and is possibly used to attract insects.

The Kingbirds are courageous fighters. Their food consists very largely of harmful insects.

7b Tail with shallow notch at end, wholly grayish-black. Fig. 182. 445 GRAY KINGBIRD. *Tyránnus dominicénsis dominicénsis.*

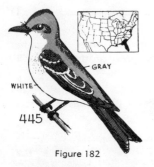

Figure 182

L. 9; W. 4.6. Somewhat larger and lighter colored than the Eastern Kingbird. Ashy gray above with wings and tail more brownish; crown with orange-red patch which is frequently concealed; under parts white with tinges of pale gray on breast; under wing-coverts pale yellow.

It inhabits most of the West India Islands and comes to our Southeast for the breeding season where it remains fairly close to salt water.

Kingbirds are often unjustly accused of killing quantities of honey bees. As a boy I knew an old beekeeper who shot every "Beebird" which same in sight. Our federal Biological Survey examines the stomach contents of many birds to determine their feeding habits. It's the only sure way. Kingbirds have thus been found to eat comparatively few honey bees and a very large percentage of these are drones. On the other hand many insect enemies of honey bees are found in their stomach contents.

Their courage and persistence in attacking crows and hawks never fails to attract attention. Of course, that is how they got their name.

8a Face streaked with black and white, tail rufous. Breast streaked (451). Larger with plain yellow breast (449). Fig. 183.

449 DERBY FLYCATCHER. *Pitángus sulphurátus derbiánus.*

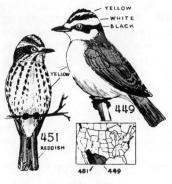

Figure 183

L. 10.5; W. 4.7. Face white and black as pictured; crówn and under parts bright yellow, throat white, wings and tail rufous.

A large bird resembling the Belted Kingfisher in size and habits. Sometimes catches small fish.

451 SULPHUR-BELLIED FLYCATCHER. *Myiodynástes luteivéntris swárthi.* L. 8.5; W. 4.6. Upper parts brownish-gray streaked with blackish; crown with large concealed bright yellow patch; chin grayish-white; other under parts sulphur yellow broadly streaked with black; tail rufous, wings blackish.

8b Face not streaked with black and white. 9

9a With two white wing-bars; tail rufous, rounded or notched. 11

9b Without wing-bars; tail square at end, crown · with orange-red patch. 10

10a Tail black with outer margins white and with no white at tip.
Fig. 184.   447 ARKANSAS KINGBIRD. *Tyránnus verticális.*

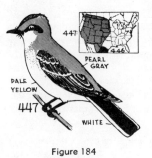

Figure 184

L. 9; W. 5. Head and back of neck plain gray, the crown with large concealed orange-red patch, wings and back gray; upper tail-coverts and tail black; chin and upper throat white becoming gray on lower throat and breast; under parts pale yellow.

446 COUCH'S KINGBIRD. *T. melanchóliclus. coúchi.* Throat white with both breast and belly yellow, tail wholly brownish and somewhat forked.

The orange-yellow patch is absent on the young birds of both of the above species.

10b Tail narrowly grayish-white tipped, with whitish side margins near tip only; back darker than in 10a. Fig. 185.

448 CASSIN'S KINGBIRD. *Tyránnus vocíferans.*

OLIVE GRAY

448

Figure 185

L. 9; W. 5.2. Head and neck slate-gray, the crown with a concealed orange-red patch; shoulders back and rump grayish-olive; tail black or brownish-black; chin white, throat and chest gray, under parts canary yellow, becoming light greenish-olive on sides; bill black.

11a Throat and chest deeper gray; tarsus relatively short; belly deep yellow. Fig. 186.

452a NORTHERN CRESTED FLYCATCHER.
Myiárchus criñítus bóreus.

YELLOW

452 A   RED-BROWN

Figure 186

L. 9; W. 4.1. Head and back olive-greenish; wings brown; primaries and tail rufous; throat and breast gray; belly sulphur yellow.

One must be sure to mention the snake skins which usually take a prominent place in the nest materials. The call, a piercing, upturning whistled *whi-i-e-e-ep* is easily recognized as it rings through the woods.

452 SOUTHERN CRESTED FLYCATCHER. *M. c. criñítus.* is found along the Atlantic coast from South Carolina through Florida.

11b Throat and chest lighter gray, belly pale yellow; tarsus relatively longer. 12

12a Tail rounded at tip. Fig. 187.

453 ARIZONA CRESTED FLYCATCHER.
Myiárchus tyránnulus magíster.

GRAYISH

PALE
YELLOW

453

FUSCOUS

Figure 187

L. 9.5; W. 4.2. Head brownish, back grayish; tail fuscous; throat and breast pale gray; belly pale yellow.

453a MEXICAN CRESTED FLYCATCHER. *M. t. nélsoni.* is quite similar to the foregoing but noticeably smaller.

82

12b Tail with notch in end; throat white; smaller than in 12a. Fig. 188.

454 ASH-THROATED FLYCATCHER.
Myiárchus cineráscens cineráscens.

Figure 188

L. 8; W. 4. Head brown darkest at middle, back relatively dark; tail mixed rufous and gray-brown, throat and upper breast very pale gray; belly pale yellow; under wing-coverts primrose yellow.

455a OLIVACEOUS FLYCATCHER. *M. tuberculifer oliváscens.* Quite similar in markings to 454 but considerably smaller in size (7.2). The throat is more definitely gray.

13a Very small Flycatcher (note size) with short bill and brownish or buff wing-bars. Fig. 189.

472 BEARDLESS FLYCATCHER. *Camptóstoma imbérbe.*

Figure 189

L. 4.5; W. 2. Grayish-olive above somewhat striped with darker on head; wings dusky; chin, throat and chest pale grayish; under parts dull yellowish-white; eyes brown.

13b Bill relatively longer; and otherwise not as in 13a. 14

14a With white or whitish bars on wing. 16

14b With no wing-bars. 15

15a Breast with narrow white stripe at center and with large dark patch on either side; tufts of white at base of rump;—not always visible. Fig. 190.

459 OLIVE-SIDED FLYCATCHER. *Nuttallórnis mesoleúcus.*

Figure 190

L. 8; W. 4.4. Slaty-olive above, sometimes smoky gray; the head and tail darker; wings blackish; large spots at sides of chest brownish-gray, as dark as back; throat and midbreast white; under parts faintly tinged with yellowish.

15b Under parts white, tinged with yellow, and becoming light grayish on sides. Fig. 191.   456 EASTERN PHOEBE Sayórnis phoébe.

Figure 191

L. 7; W. 3.4. Upper parts grayish-brown tinged with olive-green, crown and tail darker, wing-bars inconspicuous or none; under parts as in key; bill black.

Most any bridge of fair size that possesses an exposed beam or ledge is likely to house a Phoebe nest. The nest itself which may also be located on or in some domestic building is an interesting piece of construction in which mosses and lichens figure prominently. Dr. Musselman is increasing their number by putting up supports for their nests.

16a Wing over 3 inches; longer than tail. 17

16b Wing under 3 inches. 18

17a Upper parts dark olive with greenish cast; under parts whitish; belly yellowish. Fig. 192.

461 EASTERN WOOD PEWEE. Myióchanes vírens.

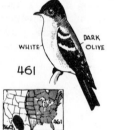

Figure 192

L. 6.5; W. 3.4. Very dark above, crown darker; wings and tail fuscous, the former with two white bars, tail notched. Upper mandible blackish, lower one yellowish or whitish.

460 COUES'S FLYCATCHER. M. pértinax pallidvéntris. L. 7.8; W. 4.3. A large gray bird of the higher mountains.

17b Grayer above than 17a and less whitish beneath, lower mandible darker. Fig. 193.

462 WESTERN WOOD PEWEE. Myióchanes ríchardsoni ríchardsoni.

Figure 193

L. 6.5; W. 3.4. Color shades as in key. Usually with no greenish tint above and scarcely any yellow below; lower mandible brownish.

The Phoebes and Pewees get their name from their calls which are rendered in a more or less mournful way.

18a Upper parts olive-green or olive brown with definite brownish tinge. 20

18b Upper parts olive-green without any tinge of brown. 19

19a Throat white, upper parts greenish. Fig. 194.

465 ACADIAN FLYCATCHER. *Empídonax viréscens.*

L. 6; W. 2.8. Dark grayish-olive-green above; tail darker; wing-bands buffy; throat and belly white; breast tinged with gray; under parts sometimes with tinges of yellow also; lower mandible whitish.

It is very tame even though it builds in secluded spots.

Figure 194

19b Throat pale yellow; breast shaded with olive-green. Fig. 195.

463 YELLOW-BELLIED FLYCATCHER. *Empídonax flavivéntris.*

L. 5.5; W. 2.5. Olive-green above, head and tail somewhat darker; wing-bands yellowish; under parts pale yellow, the breast touched with olive-green, lower mandible flesh covered to whitish. Like other members of its family it destroys many injurious insects.

Figure 195

20a Throat not yellowish. 21

20b Throat and other under parts yellowish. Fig. 196.

464 WESTERN FLYCATCHER. *Empídonax difficílis difficílis.*

L. 6; W. 3.6. Uniformly olive-brown above; definitely yellowish below; tail grayish-brown. Eye-ring white; wing-bars whitish; mandible, yellowish.

464a SAN LUCAS FLYCATCHER. *E. d. cineri-tius.* Grayer above and paler below and a bit smaller than 464.

470a BUFF-BREASTED FLYCATCHER. *E. fúl-vifrons pygmaéus.* A tiny flycatcher nesting in the mountains of southern Ariz. and N. M. Has a buff breast and white eye-ring and wing-bars.

Figure 196

85

21a Tail rather shallowly but sharply notched, eye-ring and wing-bars white; whitish below. Fig. 197.

467 LEAST FLYCATCHER. *Empídonax mínimus.*

Figure 197

L. 5.5; W. 2.5. Brownish-olive above; under parts dull white, mandible pale brownish; eye brown.

468 HAMMOND'S FLYCATCHER. *E. hámmondi.*

469 WRIGHT'S FLYCATCHER. *E. wríghti.*

469.1 GRAY FLYCATCHER. *E. gríseus.*

When one of the above three is sighted it seems to be any ones guess which one it is. All three of these western forms, are much like 467 in size and coloring.

21b Browner than 21a. Tail square cut or slightly double rounded. Fig. 198.   466a ALDER FLYCATCHER. *Empídonax traílli traílli.*

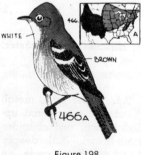

Figure 198

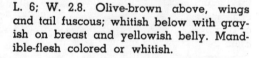

L. 6; W. 2.8. Olive-brown above, wings and tail fuscous; whitish below with grayish on breast and yellowish belly. Mandible-flesh colored or whitish.

466 LITTLE FLYCATCHER. *E. t. bréwsteri.* Somewhat browner than the foregoing. It is the western form.

These rather small members of this interesting family build their nests and live along willow or alder lined streams. The nest is often placed close to the water and is loosely put together. The 2-4 eggs have brown spots on a yellowish-buff background.

SWALLOWS
Family *Hirundinidae*

**1a Tail cut almost square at end; large light buff spot on rump.
Fig. 199.**
612 NORTHERN CLIFF SWALLOW. *Petrochelidon álbifrons álbifrons.*

L. 6; W. 4.3. Crown, back, wings and tail metallic steel blue; occasional streaks of whitish on back, forehead whitish; throat chestnut; breast and ring around neck brownish-gray; belly white.

612a LESSER CLIFF SWALLOW. *P. a. táchina.*

612b MEXICAN CLIFF SWALLOW. *P. a. melanogáster.*

Both of these are somewhat smaller than 612. The frontal patch is reddish-brown, being darker in b than a.

Figure 199

612.1a COAHUILA CLIFF SWALLOW. *P. fúlva pállida.* With buff throat; found in Central Texas.

The Cliff Swallows are highly gregarious in their nesting. Originally their much enclosed mud nests were attached to cliffs but with the coming of civilization they were quick to see the value of the eaves of barns for a nesting site. Large numbers of these earthern nests are often seen crowded on one building.

1b Tail distinctly notched. **2**

2a Tail long and deeply cut. Fig. 200.
613 BARN SWALLOW. *Hirúndo erythrogáster.*

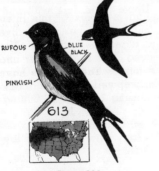

L. 7; W. 4.7; T. 3.3. Upper parts metallic steel blue; forehead, throat and upper breast reddish-brown; rest of under parts pale reddish-brown; tail deeply forked with a row of white spots on shorter feathers.

The mud nest is more open than that of the Cliff Swallow and is usually built within barns and other building instead of on the outside.

Figure 200

87

2b Notch in tail rather shallow. 3

3a Upper parts uniformly brown with no metallic luster. 6

3b Upper parts bluish or greenish with distinct metallic luster.......4

4a Under parts wholly white. 5

4b Under parts steel blue or gray. Fig. 201.

611 PURPLE MARTIN. Prógne súbis súbis.

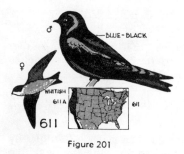

Figure 201

L. 8; W. 5.8. ♂ Glossy blue-black; wings and tail less lustrous. ♀ Upper parts much as in ♂ but duller; throat and breast brownish-gray, belly white.

611a WESTERN MARTIN. P. s. hespéria. ♂ Almost identical with 611. ♀ With larger gray areas on neck and others on back.

These almost domestic birds nested in gourds put up for them by the Indians and nest readily in the houses so often seen on poles.

5a Dark greenish-purple above with two white spots on rump. Fig. 202.
615 VIOLET-GREEN SWALLOW. Tachycinéta thalassina lépida.

Figure 202

L. 5.8; W. 4.6. Upper parts dark with metallic greenish-purple sheen; two elongated white spots on rump, much of face and entire under parts white.

This is another bird which will readily build in houses prepared by man. Findley has an interesting account of putting feathers afloat for these birds to use as nest lining, the birds catching them with an agility that is truly surprising. They lay 4 or 5 pure white eggs.

5b Green or blue-black above with metallic sheen. No spots on rump. less white on face. Fig. 203.

614 TREE SWALLOW. *Iridoprócne bícolor.*

Figure 203

L. 6; W. 4.7. Glossy greenish-blue above with sharply contrasting white beneath. The ♀ is often somewhat duller colored than the ♂. The young birds are rather dull above and sometimes grayish below.

615.1 BAHAMA SWALLOW. *Callichelídon cyaneovíridis.* Has been recorded from Southern Florida.

6a Throat and upper breast brownish-gray. Fig. 204.

617 ROUGH-WINGED SWALLOW. *Stelgidópteryx ruficóllis serripénnis.*

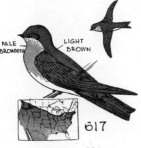

Figure 204

L. 5.8; W. 4.4. Brownish-gray above; paler brownish-gray on throat and breast; belly white. The outer web of first primary is roughened with a row of recurved hooks.

The Rough-wing is a duller colored, somewhat larger and slower flying bird than the Bank Swallow. Its nesting habits are similar to the Bank Swallow but may also build on bridges and similar structures.

6b Throat and under parts white .with dark band across breast. Fig. 205. **616 BANK SWALLOW.** *Ripária ripária ripária.*

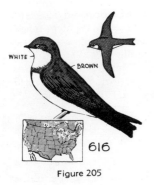

Figure 205

L. 5.2; W. 4. Brownish-gray above; extending in a narrow band across the breast otherwise white. First primary not roughened.

It digs a horizontal hole some 2 or 3 feet deep in sand banks for its nest of grass and feathers. It is somewhat smaller and more active than the Rough-wing.

CROWS, JAYS, MAGPIES
Family *Corvidae*

1a Wings long and pointed; much longer than the tail. 2

1b Wings comparitively short and rounded, at most scarcely longer than the tail often shorter. 6

2a Plumage blue; bill depressed with nostrils elongated. Fig. 206.
492 PINON JAY. *Cyanocéphalus cyanocéphalus.*

♂ L. 11; W. 6.2; T. 4.5. Dull grayish-blue, paler at throat and lower abdomen. ♀ Smaller than ♂ and duller colored (bluish-gray instead of grayish-blue). Young birds still duller with blue on wings and tail only.

These somewhat gregarious birds are friendly and unafraid. Their food consists of pinon nuts, cedar berries, grasshoppers and other insects.

Figure 206

2b Plumage black or gray; bill compressed, with nostril rounded....3

3a Plumage gray, with wings and middle tail feathers black; bill only slightly higher than broad. Fig. 207.
491 CLARKE'S NUTCRACKER. *Nucifraga columbiána.*

L. 12; W. 7.8; T. 4.6. Front of forehead, lores, eyelids and chin whitish; under tail-coverts, broad tips of secondaries and outer tail feathers white; the black of wings and tail with purplish-blue or violet sheen. The gray of winter birds drab or smoky and darker than the brownish-gray of summer.

Figure 207

3b Plumage black (sometimes with metallic sheen); bill much higher than broad. 4

90

4a Larger than 4b. Feathers of throat elongated, distinct in outline. Wings held horizontal when soaring. Fig. 208.

486a NORTHERN RAVEN. Córvus córax principális.

486

486

.: 487

486

Figure 208

L. 25; W. 17; T. 10. Glossy black with metallic tinges of purplish, bluish or bronze. Base of neck feathers gray.

486 AMERICAN RAVEN. C. c. sinuátus much like 486a but averaging smaller; bill relatively smaller and narrower.

487 WHITE-NECKED RAVEN. C. cryptoleúcus. Definitely smaller than 486 with shorter and deeper bill. Base of neck feathers white.

4b Feathers of throat short and blended; wings tilted upward when soaring. CROWS. 5

5a Larger; call a definite "caw". Fig. 209.

488 EASTERN CROW. Córvus brachyrhýnchos brachyrhýnchos.

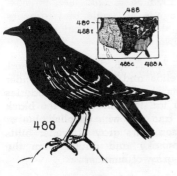

488

489 –
488 f

488 c   488 A

488

Figure 209

L. 19; W. 13. Deep black with metallic tinges of violet and greenish-blue.

488a FLORIDA CROW. C. b. páscuus. Smaller than 488 with relatively larger bill and feet.

488b WESTERN CROW. C. b. hésperis. Still smaller than 488a.

488c SOUTHERN CROW. C. b. paúlus. Smaller than 488.

489 NORTHWESTERN CROW. C. b. caurínus. Smallest of these 4. (L. 16; W. 11.5.)

Crows are likely our shrewdest and most intelligent birds. Many stories are told of the clever things they do.

5b Call of adult "car". Smaller than any 488. Fig. 210.

490 FISH CROW. Córvus ossífragus.

490

Figure 210

L. 15; W. 11. Back feathers uniformly dull black without dull margins as in 488.

As the name indicates much of its food consists of fish part of which it catches but most of which are the dead fish washed up along shore. It is highly destructive in eating the eggs of other birds.

6a Tail but little if any longer than the wing. 7

6b Tail much longer than wing, widest near its middle. Fig. 211.

475 AMERICAN MAGPIE. Píca píca hudsónia.

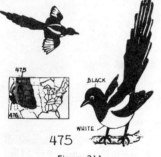

475

Figure 211

L. 20; W. 8; T. 11. Bill black; back and breast velvety black, wings shining blue-black; tail above greenish; belly, scapulars and inner margins of primaries white.

476 YELLOW-BILLED MAGPIE. P. nútalli. Smaller than 475. (L. 18.) and with yellow bill and eye-space.

The Magpies are flesh eaters and often cause annoyance to cattlemen in picking at wounds on cattle and trappers by eating the bait or the catch.

7a Back green or bluish-green. Fig. 212.

483 GREEN JAY. Xanthoúra luxuósa glaucéscens.

483

Figure 212

L. 11; W. 4.5. Top of head and patch under eye blue; wings, back and central tail feathers green; outer tail feathers yellow; under parts greenish-yellow; throat black.

This beautiful bird invades but a small portion of our country. It like others of its family is a robber of other birds nests.

7b Without markings of green. 8

8a Marked in part with blue. 9

8b Marked with gray, black and white. Fig. 213.
484 CANADA JAY. *Perisóreus canadénsis canadénsis.*

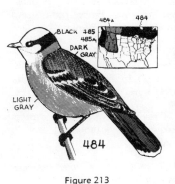

Figure 213

L. 12; W. 5.8. Forehead, chin, throat and chest white. Other head parts as pictured blackish-slate; back rump and upper tail-coverts mouse gray, wings and tail slate-gray; under parts light gray.

484a ROCKY MOUNTAIN JAY. *P. c. capitalis.* White area on head considerably larger.

485 OREGON JAY. *P. obscúrus obscúrus.*

485a GRAY JAY. *P. o. griseus.*

Both are smaller and lighter colored than the Canada Jay. 485 ranges along the coast while the Gray Jay lives farther inland.

9a With a distinct pointed crest. 10

9b Not crested. 11

10a Under parts whitish, interrupted by a black collar, some feathers of wing and tail white tipped as pictured. Fig. 214.
477 NORTHERN BLUE JAY. *Cyanocitta cristata cristata.*

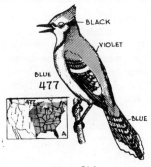

Figure 214

L. 11.7; W. 5.2. Grayish-blue above with markings of black and white as mentioned in key.

477a FLORIDA BLUE JAY. *C. c. florincola,* is much like 477 but smaller (L. 10.) with paler and duller color, and the white areas at tips of feathers smaller.

477b SEMPLE'S BLUE JAY. *C. c. semplei.* Lives in the southern tip of Florida.

10b Under parts blue sometimes blackish in front; no white tipped feathers in wings or tail. Fig. 215.

478 STELLER'S JAY. *Cyanocítta stélleri stélleri.*

L. 13; W. 6.2. Head and neck black or slaty-gray. Forehead usually streaked with blue.

478a BLUE-FRONTED JAY. *C. s. frontális,* is similar with back paler and head and neck grayish-brown.

478b LONG-CRESTED JAY. *C. s. dia demáta,* has a longer crest, bluish-white streaks on forehead and a white spot over the eye.

478c BLACK-HEADED JAY. *C. s. annéctans* is marked like preceding but is darker in color.

Figure 215

478e COAST JAY. *C. s. carbonácea.* Smaller and paler than 478.

11a Tail longer than wing; a definite black area below and behind the eye. **12**

11b Tail definitely shorter than wing; side of head blue; under parts rather uniformly blue-gray, without white patch on throat. Fig. 216.

482 ARIZONA JAY. *Aphelócoma siéberi arizónae.*

L. 13; W. 6.7; T. 6. Grayish-blue above, head, wings and tail brighter blue. No stripes or bands on under parts.

482a COUCH'S JAY. *A. s. couchi.* Somewhat smaller with upper parts bluer than 482; throat pale; bill more slender. The Arizona Jay seems to be about the most curious and harshly noisy of all the Jays, and that is saying much. Their shallow nests are built in trees. The blue eggs number 4 to 7. The food consists of acorns, nuts and insects.

Figure 216

12a A definite white patch in throat with feeble blackish band below. Fig. 217.

481 CALIFORNIA JAY. *Aphelócoma califórnica califórnica.*

Figure 217

L. 12; W. 4.8. Head and neck, on sides and behind, dark cobalt blue; back drab gray; wings and tail blue. Chin, throat and chest pure white; under parts light gray.

Several subspecies are named but their differences do not lend themselves to field recognition. 481b BELDING'S JAY. *A. c. obscúra;* 481c LONG-TAILED JAY. *A. c. immánis;* 481d NICASIO JAY. *A. c. oocléptica* (small area around San Francisco); 480 WOODHOUSE'S JAY. *A. c. woódhousei;* 480.2 TEXAS JAY. *A. c. texána.*

12b Without pure white patch in throat. Fig. 218.

479 FLORIDA JAY. *Aphelócoma coeruléscens.*

Figure 218

L. 11.5; W. 4.5; T. 5.6. Head, wings and tail, blue; back and rump grayish-drab; throat and chest light gray; lower chest and under parts pale blue; legs and feet black; eyes brown. Young birds mouse gray above; under parts dull whitish.

There are many species of Jays widely scattered throughout almost the whole world. Their aggressive quarrelsome life make them well known, "As noisy as a Jay" is a well understood saying. The Blue Jay is one of our best known American birds.

Structurally the Jays are near relatives of the Crows and the two groups have many common habits.

TITMICE
Family *Paridae*

1a Head with distinct crest. 2

1b Head without a crest. 4

2a Throat white or gray; neck and side of head without black markings. 3

2b Throat and face marked with black as pictured. Fig. 219.
        734 BRIDLED TITMOUSE. *Baeólophus wóllweberi annéxus.*

Figure 219

L. 5; W. 2.6. Upper parts gray; under parts grayish-white, with buffy tinge on abdomen in winter. Head and neck black and white as pictured; bill black.

The five to seven tiny white eggs are laid in a down lined nest in some natural tree cavity.

3a Upper parts slate-gray; head with either blackish or rusty markings. Fig. 220.
        731 TUFTED TITMOUSE. *Baeólophus bícolor.*

Figure 220

L. 6; W. 3.3. Forehead black or sooty. Black line on upper eye-lid making eyes appear large. Upper parts, slate-gray; under parts dull white with light reddish-brown on sides and flanks; bill black.

Its call is a loud and easily remembered whistled "Peter-Peter-Peter." West Virginia has chosen it for their state bird.

732 BLACK CRESTED TITMOUSE. *B. atricristátus atricristátus.* L. 5.5; W. 2.8. Much like 731 except that the crest is black, with the forehead dull white, sometimes tinged with brown.

732a SENNETT'S TITMOUSE. *B. a. sénnetti,* is similar to 732 but noticeably larger.

3b Upper parts brownish-gray or gray-brown; no black or rust on head. Fig. 221.

733 **PLAIN TITMOUSE.** *Bae6lophus inornâtus inornâtus.*

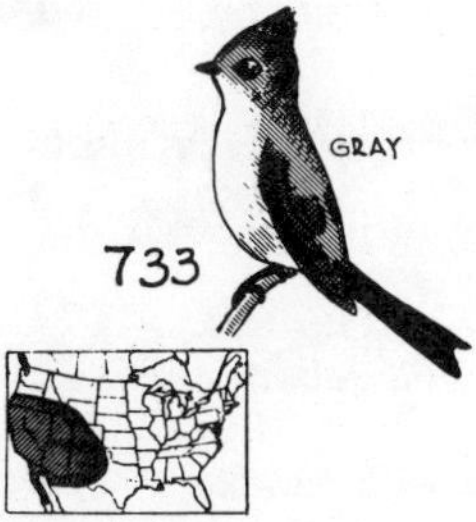

733

GRAY

Figure 221

L. 5.3; W. 2.7. Face and under parts pale brownish-gray to dull grayish-white; bill grayish.

Three subspecies as listed below are named for our area, but since their variations in size or intensity of color and their distribution varies with the season no attempt is made to indicate their range. The area marked on the map is the combined distribution of all subspecies of 733.

733a **GRAY TITMOUSE.** *B. i. gríseus.*

733c **OREGON TITMOUSE.** *B. i. sequestrátus.*

734d **SAN DIEGO TITMOUSE.** *B. i. transpositus.*

4a Top of head not marked with yellow. 5

4b Top of head yellowish. Fig. 222.

746 **ARIZONA VERDIN.** *Auríparus flâviceps flâviceps.*

YELLOWISH
RED BROWN
GRAY

746

Figure 222

L. 4.3; W. 2.2. Head, chin and throat yellow; back brownish-gray, wings and tail darker with chestnut wing coverts; under parts light brownish-gray. Young birds lack the yellow on the head and chestnut spot on bend of wing. The nest is a covered affair of twigs and stems and has the opening in the side.

5a Top of head black. 8

5b Top of head brown or brownish. 6

6a Throat, chest and under parts pale gray or whitish. Fig. 223.
743 COAST BUSH-TIT. *Psaltríparus mínimus mínimus.*

743

Figure 223

L. 4; W. 1.9; T. 2.1. Top of head brownish drab; above smoky-gray; wings and tail often darker. Tail longer than wing; bill very short. Very active little birds feeding and traveling in flocks.

743a CALIFORNIA BUSH-TIT. *P. m. califórnicus.* Interior valleys of Calif.

744 LEAD COLORED BUSH-TIT. *P. m. plúmbeus.* Ranges through the Rocky Mountain region; cheeks of the ♂ brown.

745 LLOYD'S BUSH-TIT. *P. m. lloýdi.* The male's cheeks marked with black.

6b Throat and chest with wide black bib. 7

7a Back grayish-brown. Fig. 224.
740 HUDSONIAN CHICKADEE. *Penthéstes hudsónicus hudsónicus.*

740

Figure 224

L. 5.3; W. 2.5; T. 2.4. Head grayish-brown, upper parts lighter gray-brown; wings and tail dull slate; under parts white to pale gray with a cinnamon-brown patch at side.

740a ACADIAN CHICKADEE. *P. h. littorális.* Smaller than #740 with upper parts a bit more brown.

740b COLUMBIAN CHICKADEE. *P. h. columbiánus.* Upper parts less brown than #740 and with larger bill.

7b Back chestnut. Fig. 225.

741 CHESTNUT-BACKED CHICKADEE.
Penthéstes ruféscens ruféscens.

741

Figure 225

L. 4.8; W. 2.5. Cap sepia brown; upper parts chestnut; wings and tail brownish-gray; under parts white with sides chestnut.

741a NICASIO CHICKADEE. *P. r. neglēctus.* Chestnut color paler and chestnut area on sides smaller.

741b BARLOW'S CHICKADEE. *P. r. bárlowi.* Sides pale gray instead of chestnut. The two subspecies have a very limited range in California.

8a With white stripe above eye as pictured. Fig. 226.
  738 MOUNTAIN CHICKADEE. *Penthéstes gámbeli gámbeli.*

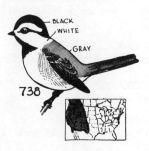

Figure 226

L. 5.5; W. 2.8. Top of head and throat black; back, wings and tail gray; under parts white to light gray.

The following subspecies closely resemble each other. Their ranges have seasonal variations. No attempt is hade here to show their distribution. The map shows the composit range of these several subspecies.

738a BAILEY'S CHICKADEE. *P. g. báileyae.*

738b GRINNELL'S CHICKADEE. *P. g. grinnélli.*

738c SHORT-TAILED CHICKADEE. *P. g. abbreviátus.*

738e INYO CHICKADEE. *P. g. inyoénsis.*

8b Without white stripe above eye. 9

9a Lower black feathers of throat with white tips giving bib a fringed effect; tail long. Fig. 227.
  735 BLACK-CAPPED CHICKADEE. *Penthéstes atricapíllus atricapíllus.*

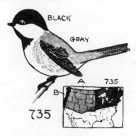

Figure 227

L. 5; W. 2.7; T. 2.5. Head and throat black as pictured; back, wings and tail slate-gray; sides of head and neck and under parts of body white. It is the state bird of both Maine and Massachusets.

735a LONG-TAILED CHICKADEE. *P. a. septentrionális.* Larger than #735 with wings and tail plainly longer; paler in color.

735b OREGON CHICKADEE. *P. a. occidentális.* Smaller and darker than #735.

9b Lower feathers of bib wholly black, forming sharp line between bib and white of chest; tail shorter. Fig. 228.

736 CAROLINA CHICKADEE. *Penthéstes carolinénsis carolinénsis.*

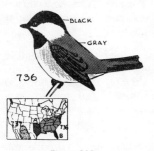

736

Figure 228

L. 4.5; W. 2.4; T. 2.1. Colors darker than in #735 with little or no white in wings and tail. Bill larger.

736a PLUMBEOUS CHICKADEE. *P. c. ágilis.* Larger than 736 with gray parts paler.

736b FLORIDA CHICKADEE. *P. c. ímpiger.* Smaller and darker than #736.

737 MEXICAN CHICKADEE. *P. sclateri eidos.* Similar to #736 but larger and darker; sides olive-gray.

NUTHATCHES
Family *Sittidae*

1a Side of head and neck not wholly white. 2

1b Side of head and neck entirely white. Fig. 229.

727 WHITE-BREASTED NUTHATCH. *Sítta carolinénsis carolinénsis.*

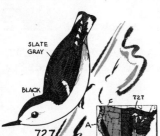

727

Figure 229

L. 5.5; W. 3.7. Upper parts blue-gray with black cap and other black and white markings as pictured. Under parts white; sides brownish. Its characteristic "yank, yank" call as it goes about its search for food helps to locate it.

727a SLENDER-BILLED NUTHATCH. *S. c. aculeáta.* Bill a bit longer and more slender and the gray somewhat darker than 727.

727b FLORIDA NUTHATCH. *S. c. átkinsi.* A bit smaller and darker than 727.

727c ROCKY MOUNTAIN NUTHATCH. *S. c. nélsoni.* Similar to 727a but larger and with heavier

727e INYO NUTHATCH. *S. c. tenuíssima.*

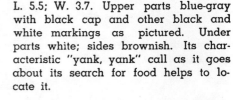

2a Cap olive or brown and covering eye. 3

2b Cap black, not covering eye, but with black streak running "through" the eye. Fig. 230.

728 RED-BREASTED NUTHATCH. *Sítta canadénsis.*

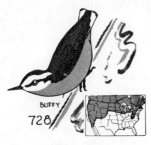

Figure 230

L. 4.5; W. 2.7. Upper parts bluish-gray with black markings. Chin and throat dull white changing to light buff and dull reddish-buff on under parts.

This bird is readily distinguished from the White-breasted Nuthatch by the black stripe through its eye and its smaller size. In a rather erratic migration it reaches our southern borders.

All of the Nuthatches have the unique habit of examining tree trunks from top to bottom travelling head down.

3a Cap and back of neck brown, with large white spot on middle of neck. Fig. 231.

729 BROWN-HEADED NUTHATCH. *Sítta pusílla pusílla.*

Figure 231

L. 4.5; W. 2.5. Back and wings blue-gray; tail black with markings of white and gray; under parts white or whitish, tinged with buff.

729a GRAY-HEADED NUTHATCH. *S. p. cániceps.* Smaller than 729 but much the same color.

3b Cap and back of neck olive, spot at back of neck pale if at all apparent. Fig. 232.

730 PYGMY NUTHATCH. *Sitta pygmaéa pygmaéa.*

Figure 232

L. 4.5; W. 2.7. Back, wings and tail blue-gray marked with black and white as pictured; under parts buffy-white.

730a WHITE-NAPED NUTHATCH. *S. p. leuconúcha.* Larger than 730, especially the bill. Pale spot on neck larger.

730b BLACK-EARED NUTHATCH. *S. p. melanótis.* Head a bit grayer than 730.

WRENS
Family *Troglodytidae*

1a With more or less conspicuous line over (or through) eye. 3

1b Face without a line over eye. 2

2a Throat and breast white; belly dark reddish-brown. Fig. 233.
      717a CANON WREN. *Cathérpes mexicánus conspérsus.*

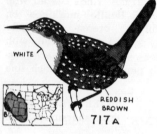

Figure 233

L. 6; W. 2.4. Upper parts and belly dark reddish-brown thickly set with fine white . dots, occasionally absent; tail with narrow black crossbars; throat and upper chest wholly white; eyes brown.

717b DOTTED WREN. *C. m. punctulátus.* Similar in size and markings to the Canon Wren but darker in color.

2b Throat and breast dull white tinged with dusky; belly dull white, faintly barred at sides. Fig. 234.
      721 EASTERN HOUSE WREN. *Troglódytes aédon aédon.*

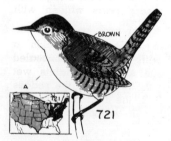

Figure 234

L. 5; W. 2. Upper parts brown; wings and tail rather indistinctly barred with black; no markings on face; under tail-coverts mixed rusty-brown and white with black bars; eye brown.

721a WESTERN HOUSE WREN. *T. a. párkmani.* Similar to 721 but a bit larger, grayer and paler.

Wrens live an exceedingly busy life during the nesting season. The normal brood is 6 - 8. More than a thousand trips with tiny worms and such, per day is required to keep them content and growing. The female seems to do most of the work but when the mother at our Wrenhouse was accidentally killed one summer her mate arose to the occasion and fed his little orphans until they were grown.

4a Under tail-coverts barred; head and back plain. Fig. 235.
     722 EASTERN WINTER WREN. *Nánnus hiemális hiemális.*

Figure 235

L. 4; W. 1.8. Upper parts uniformly dark brown; tail and wings barred with black and with white markings on primaries; throat, breast and belly brownish-gray, the latter barred with darker at sides; under tail-coverts rusty-brown with black bars; blackish line through eye.

722a WESTERN WINTER WREN. *N. h. pacíficus.* Darker than the above and more richly colored.

4b Under tail-coverts plain brownish-buff; head and back more or less obscurely striped. Fig. 236.
     724 SHORT-BILLED MARSH WREN. *Cistothórus stelláris.*

Figure 236

L. 4; W. 1.8. Above buffy-brown streaked with black and whitish; wings and tail barred; under parts whitish with buff on sides.

This interesting little wren builds a round nest with a rather concealed opening at one side. It inhabits wet meadows and builds among the sedges or cat-tails. Both the bird and its nest are rather difficult to locate.

6b Breast neither striped or spotted. Fig. 237.

719 BEWICK'S WREN. *Thryománes bewicki bewicki.*

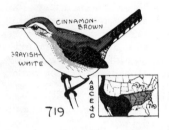

Figure 237

L. 5; W. 2.3. Plain dark cinnamon brown above; tail rounded when spread; central tail feathers grayish, barred with black; outer tail feathers plain black tipped with whitish; grayish white below with brownish flanks.

719a VIGOR'S WREN. *T. b. spilúrus.* Larger and browner than 719.

719b BAIRD'S WREN. *T. b. eremóphilus.* Smaller than 719.

719c TEXAS WREN. *T. b. crýptus.* Larger and grayer than 719.

719d SOOTY WREN. *T. b. charientúrus.* Dull olive-brown above and quite small.

719e SEATTLE WREN. *T. b. calophónus.* A bit smaller than 719; deep sepia above.

719g SAN JOAQUIN WREN. *T. b. drymoécus.* Smaller than 719; strong brownish above.

No attempt has been made to separate the ranges of the western subspecies.

7a Heavily spotted on breast; larger than any of our other wrens. Fig. 238.

713 NORTHERN CACTUS WREN. *Heleódytes brunneicapíllus couési.*

Figure 238

L. 8; W. 3.5. Brownish above more or less streaked or spotted with white; upper tail-coverts and middle tail feathers gray, barred with dusky; outer tail feathers barred black and white; throat and chest white heavily spotted with black; eye red. This is Arizona's state bird.

713a BRYANT'S CACTUS WREN. *H. b. brýanti.* Darker; back browner and more streaked with white.

7b Spots on breast forming streaks; tail tipped with **buff; smaller.** Fig. 239.

715 COMMON ROCK WREN. *Salpínctes obsolétus obsolétus.*

L. 6; W. 2.8. Above grayish-brown with numerous small dusky and whitish specks; mid-tail lightly barred with dusky; tip marked with black and buff as pictured. Under parts white to buffy, more or less streaked with gray-brown; eye brown.

Figure 239

8a Back unstreaked bright rusty-brown. Fig. 240.

718 CAROLINA WREN. *Thryothórus ludoviciánus ludoviciánus.*

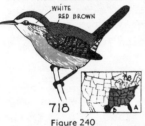

L. 5.8; W. 2.4. Above plain rufous or red-brown; wings and tail duller brown rather obscurely barred with dusky, under parts buffy white; under tail-coverts buff strongly barred with black; eye brown.

718a FLORIDA WREN. *T. l. miaménsis.* More richly colored and larger.

718b LOMITA WREN. *T. l. lomiténsis.* Much duller colored than 718.

Figure 240

8b Conspicuous black and white stripes on back as pictured. Fig. 241.

725 LONG-BILLED MARSH WREN. *Telmatódytes palústris palústris.*

L. 5; W. 2. Upper parts brown, more blackish on head, back striped as in key; under parts dull white tinged with brown at sides; under tail-coverts pale brown varying from unmarked to barred with dusky; eye brown.

725a TULE WREN. *T. p. paludícola.* Deeper brown and with longer tail.

725b WORTHINGTON'S MARSH WREN. *T. p. gríseus.* Smaller than 725 and grayer.

Figure 241

725c WESTERN MARSH WREN. *T. p. plésius.* Somewhat larger and a bit redder than 725.

725d PRAIRIE MARSH WREN. *T. p. dissaëptus.* A bit larger and more reddish than 725.

725e MARIAN'S MARSH WREN. *T. p. mariánae.* Smaller and considerably darker.

725f ALBERTA MARSH WREN. *T. p. láíngi.* Somewhat larger and darker.

725g SUISUN MARSH WREN. *T. p. aestuarínus.* Somewhat lighter colored.

725h LOUISIANA MARSH WREN. *T. p. thryóphilus.* Quite small and pale colored.

MOCKINGBIRDS and THRASHERS
Family *Mimidae*

1a Bill long, curved, "sickle-like." 2

1b Bill not sickle-shaped. 5

2a Under parts specked; outer tail feathers tipped with white. Fig. 242.
  707 CURVE-BILLED THRASHER. *Toxóstoma curviróstre curviróstre.*

Figure 242

L. 11; W. 4.3. Brownish or drab gray above; wings often with narrow white wing-bars; under parts buffy-white to pale brownish, spotted with pale brownish-gray; bill dark; eye orange-yellow.

707a PALMER'S THRASHER. *T. c. pálmeri.* A bit larger than the above; without white spots at end of tail.

707b BROWNSVILLE THRASHER. *T. c. oberhólseri.*

708 BENDIRE'S THRASHER. *T. béndirei.* Much like 707a but browner above and spots on breast, smaller.

2b Under parts plain, without specks; tail not tipped with white.....3
3a Belly bright cinnamon-buff; dull gray-brown above. Fig. 243.
  710 CALIFORNIA THRASHER. *Toxóstoma redivívum redivívum.*

Figure 243

L. 12.4; W. 4.1. Deep grayish-brown above; the tail and its upper coverts nearly sepia; chin and throat pale buff deepening into cinnamon-buff on abdomen and cinnamon on under tail-coverts; bill blackish; eye brown.

710b SONOMA THRASHER. *T. r. sonomae.*

3b Not as in 3a. 4

4a Under tail-coverts cinnamon-rufous; upper parts dark. Fig. 244.
   712 CRISSAL THRASHER. *Toxóstoma dorsále dorsále.*

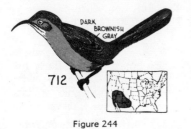

Figure 244

L. 12; W. 4. Plain grayish-brown above; tail darker; throat dull white passing into red-brown on flanks and under tail-coverts; bill black; eye brown.

This bird of the desert is apparently unusually shy for a thrasher. It nests in bushes near the ground.

4b Under tail-coverts buff; upper parts pale. Fig. 245.
   711 LECONTE'S THRASHER. *Toxóstoma lecóntei lecóntei.*

Figure 245

L. 11; W. 3.9. Pale grayish-brown above; the tail somewhat darker; under parts dull whitish becoming deep buff on hind flanks and under tail-coverts; bill black; eye red-brown.

711a DESERT THRASHER. *T. l. arenícola.* Upper parts somewhat darker and grayer than the above.

This bird is an exceptionally fine singer. Like the Mockingbird it continues to sing through the night.

5a Slate-gray with black cap and tail and rust-red under tail-coverts.
   Fig. 246.   **704 CATBIRD.** *Dumetélla carolinénsis.*

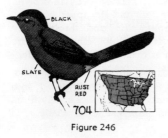

Figure 246

L. 9; W. 3.6. Wholly slate-gray except crown and tail which are black and under tail-coverts, rust-red.

This friendly bird is well known about the home garden. It usually builds in bushes and lays 3-5 shining dark green-blue eggs. In its widely varied song it does not at all repeat each syllable as does the Brown Thrasher. Its occasional cat-like call gives it its name.

5b Not as in 5a. 6

6a Principal color gray. 7

6b Principal color bright rufous-brown. Fig. 247.
705 BROWN THRASHER. *Toxóstoma rúfum.*

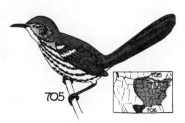

Figure 247

L. 11.5; W. 4. Rufous above; wings with 2 white bars; white to buffy beneath, prominently streaked with dark brown. The 3-6 pale bluish-white eggs, thickly set with very fine red-brown specks are laid in fairly large nests in bushes.

It is a master of bird song, its repetition of each syllable readily distinguishes it from the Catbird. It is the state bird of Georgia.

706 SENNETT'S THRASHER. *T. longi-róstre sénnetti.* Less rufous and with black streaks on breast; otherwise much the same as 705.

7a Outer tail feathers wholly white; breast plain. Fig. 248.
703 EASTERN MOCKINGBIRD. *Mímus polyglóttos polyglóttos.*

Figure 248

L. 10.5; W. 4.5. Ashy-gray above; wings and tail blackish-slate, marked with white as pictured. Pale smoky gray with some buff beneath. The white areas in the ♂ are larger than in the ♀. This popular bird is claimed by Arkansas, Florida, Mississippi, South Carolina, Tennessee and Texas.

703a WESTERN MOCKINGBIRD. *M. p. leucópterus.* Somewhat larger and paler with stronger buff on belly.

It is an expert in song and in imitation. Its way of shooting up into the air and floating back down as it sings is highly characteristic.

7b Outer tail feathers white only at tip; breast spotted or streaked. Fig. 249.   702 SAGE THRASHER. *Oreoscóptes montánus.*

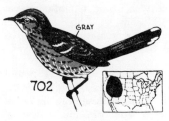

Figure 249

L. 8.5; W. 4. Grayish-brown above, somewhat indistinctly streaked; wings and tail darker, marked with white as pictured; under parts streaked with grayish-brown or sooty; bill dark; eye lemon-yellow.

This bird belongs to the deserts and open country. It builds near the ground in bushes.

THRUSHES, BLUEBIRDS, SOLITAIRES
Family *Turdidae*

1a At least the tail and wings blue or bluish. 2

1b Without markings of blue. 4

2a Breast pale (turquoise) blue, (brownish-gray in ♀). Fig. 250.
          768 MOUNTAIN BLUEBIRD. *Siália corrucoídes.*

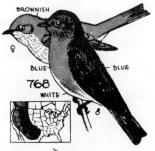

Figure 250

L. 7.3; W. 4.7. ♂ Cerulean-blue above, the wings and tail a bit darker. Chin, throat, breast and sides turquoise blue, belly and under tail-coverts white; bill black; eye dark brown. ♀ Much paler than ♂ with head, back and scapulars smoke gray; under parts pale brownish-gray; belly white. Both Idaho and Nevada have made this species their state bird.

2b Breast reddish. 3

3a Back wholly blue (often pale in ♀). Fig. 251.
766 EASTERN BLUEBIRD. *Siália siális siális.*

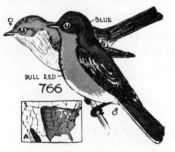

Figure 251

L. 7; W. 4. ♂ Bright blue above; throat grayish, breast cinnamon-rufous; belly white. ♀ Paler and grayer than ♂. The immature birds have speckled breasts.

It will nest readily in boxes if not annoyed too much by English Sparrows. Dr. T. E. Musselman, the well known "Bird Man" of Quincy, Illinois, has erected literally hundreds of blue bird houses along country roads (usually on fence posts) and has a very high percentage of occupancy. He figures that approximately 5000 young birds are reared in his boxes each year. It is the state bird of New York and Missouri.

766a AZURE BLUEBIRD. *S. s. fúlva.* Upper parts with more greenish tinge; paler below and with longer tail than the above.

3b Back with a rust-red area same as breast (rarely wholly blue) (♀ paler and duller). Fig. 252.
767 WESTERN BLUEBIRD. *Siália mexicána occidentális.*

Figure 252

L. 7; W. 4.2. ♂ Cobalt or ultramarine blue and rust-red, as pictured; bill black; eye brown. ♀ Largely brownish-gray above except tail which is blue; under parts light grayish-brown.

767a CHESTNUT-BACKED BLUEBIRD. *S. m. baírdi.* ♂ With entire back and scapulars rust-red and larger red area below. ♀ More reddish above than 767.

767b SAN PEDRO BLUEBIRD. *S. m. anabélae.* ♂ The blue, ultramarine; ♀ back and scapulars gray-brown.

4a Breast reddish. 5

4b Breast not marked with reddish. 6

5a With band of slate-black crossing chest (rarely broken). Fig. 253.
    763 PACIFIC VARIED THRUSH. *Ixóreus naévius naévius.*

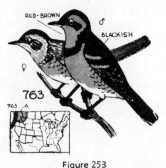

Figure 253

L. 10; W. 5. ♂ Plain slate above, the head often darker; reddish or tawny and white beneath and on face above eye; slate-black band across chest. ♀ Marked similar to ♂ but with duller colors.

763a NORTHERN VARIED THRUSH. *I. n. meruloídes.* Highly similar to 763.

5b Breast wholly reddish without cross band. Fig. 254.
    761 EASTERN ROBIN. *Túrdus migratórius migratórius.*

Figure 254

L. 10; W. 5.5. ♂ Upper parts gray, head black; under parts reddish and white. Outer tail-feathers prominently tipped with white; bill yellow, eye brown. ♀ Head grayish and entire bird somewhat paler. Young with very much speckled breast. It has been adopted as state bird by Connecticut, Michigan, Virginia and Wisconsin.

761a WESTERN ROBIN. *T. m. propínquus.* Somewhat paler than 761.

761b SOUTHERN ROBIN. *T. m. achrústerus.* Smaller in size and paler and duller in color.

761c NORTHWESTERN ROBIN. *T. m. caurínus.*

111

6a Brownish back; under parts spotted or streaked; no white on tail...7

6b Back grayish; under parts plain without markings; outer tail-feathers largely white. Fig. 255.

754 TOWNSEND'S SOLITAIRE. *Myadéstes tównsendi.*

Figure 255

L. 9; W. 4.7. Drab-gray to brown-gray above, wings and tail darker; under parts same color but lighter. Eye ringed with dull white; wing and upper tail-coverts marked with buff; bill black; eye brown.

This bird a bit smaller than a Wood Thrush acts much like a Robin. Its nest is built on the ground often along streams.

7a Tail reddish-brown; brighter than head and back. Fig. 256.

759b EASTERN HERMIT THRUSH. *Hylocíchla guttáta fáxoni.*

Figure 256

L. 7.2; W. 3.5. Olive-brown above; tail pale rufous, throat and breast buffy, belly white becoming pale gray at sides; breast with large round black spots, elongated markings in throat. It is the state bird of Vermont.

759a AUDUBON'S HERMIT THRUSH. *H. g. aúduboni.* Larger than the above and paler.

759c DWARF HERMIT THRUSH. *H. g. nánus.* Similar in color but smaller than 759b.

759d MONTEREY HERMIT THRUSH. *H. g. slévina.* Pale colored and smaller than 759b.

759e SIERRA HERMIT THRUSH. *H. g. sequoiénsis.* The size of 759b and paler in color.

759f MONO HERMIT THRUSH. *H. g. polionóto.*

7b Not as in 7a. 8

8a Reddish-brown above. 9

8b Olive above. 10

9a Head and back brighter than tail; round black dots rather thickly scattered over entire under parts. Fig. 257.

755 WOOD THRUSH. *Hylocíchla mustelína.*

Figure 257

L. 8.3; W. 4.5. Bright cinnamon-brown above, head brightest, becoming olive-brown on tail. White beneath with large round black dots and black lines in throat. The Wood Thrush is loved by all for its clear sparkling song and friendly ways. The District of Columbia claims it.

9b Throat and upper breast buffy marked with triangular brown spots; belly white. Fig. 258.

756 VEERY. *Hylocíchla fuscéscens fuscéscens.*

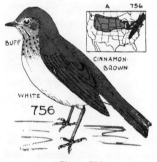

Figure 258

L. 7.5; W. 3.8. Upper parts including wings and tail rather uniform cinnamon brown; less bright than the Wood Thrush. Throat white at center, its sides and upper breast creamy buff; markings black, wedge-shaped; belly white.

756a WILLOW THRUSH. *H. f. salicicóla.* Somewhat darker above than the Veery.

10a Throat and breast white; lores grayish. Fig. 259.

757 GRAY-CHEEKED THRUSH. *Hylocíchla mínima alíciae.*

Figure 259

L. 7.6; W. 4.1. Uniformly olive above; eye ring whitish; marks black, those on sides of throat wedge-shaped, round on breast.

757a BICKNELL'S THRUSH. *H. m. mínima.* Almost identical in markings with the preceeding but a bit smaller.

10b Eye-ring, lores, throat and breast creamy buff. Fig. 260.
758α OLIVE-BACKED THRUSH. *Hylocíchla ustuláta swaínsoni.*

Figure 260

L. 7.2; W. 4. Wholly olive above; lores and eye-ring cream buff; under parts buff; wedge-shaped spots, on throat and round ones on breast; mid-belly white. Stewart Edward White who made an intensive study of the song and habits of this bird found that it repeated its song over 4000 times each day.

758 RUSSET-BACKED THRUSH. *H. u. ustuláta.* Browner above and a bit larger than 758α.

KINGLETS and GNATCATCHERS
Family *Sylviidae*

1a Olive or olive-greenish above; wing-bars conspicuous; tail short, forked. 2

1b Back blue-gray; tail long, black and white. 3

2a Head plain, or with often concealed red tuft; white eye-ring. Fig. 261.

749 EASTERN RUBY-CROWNED KINGLET. *Corthýlio caléndula caléndula.*

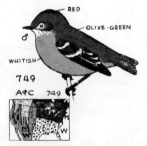

Figure 261

L. 4.4; W. 2.2. ♂ Upper parts grayish-olive-green, wings and tail darker; crown with brilliant red tuft which is often alternately concealed and displayed; under parts whitish, slightly tinged with buff. ♀ Much the same as male but lacking the red crest.

749α SITKA KINGLET. *C. c. grinnélli.* Darker with somewhat longer bill.

749c WESTERN RUBY-CROWNED KINGLET. *C. c. ineráceus.* Lighter colored than 749 with shorter bill. It should be noted that while this subspecies is confined to the territory marked for it on the map, the Eastern Ruby-Crown invades much of this same western territory also, in its breeding, migration and wintering. The Kinglets are very tame; they are excellent singers.

114

2b Crown bright vermilion bordered with yellow (♂), or wholly yellow (♀). Whitish line over eye. Fig. 262.

748 EASTERN GOLDEN-CROWNED KINGLET.
Régulus sátrapa sátrapa.

Figure 262

L. 4.1; W. 2.1. ♂ Upper parts olive-green, wings and tail darker; under parts dusky whitish; crown with mid-stripe of vermilion bordered on each side with a stripe of yellow, then one of black. ♀ Similar to ♂ but lacking the vermilion stripe on head.

748a WESTERN GOLDEN-CROWNED KINGLET. *R. s. olivĂĄceus.* More greenish with shorter wings and tail.

3a Upper part of head black. (head slate-gray in female). Fig. 263.

752 PLUMBEOUS GNATCATCHER. *Polióptila melanúra melanúra.*

Figure 263

L. 4.5; W. 1.8. ♂ A tiny slender bird with back bluish slate-gray, wings duller. Head and tail glossy black as pictured; margins of tail white. Under parts very light becoming pure white on belly. ♀ Rump brownish-gray, head slate-gray; otherwise like ♂ .

753 BLACK-TAILED GNATCATCHER. *P. m. califórnica.* Under parts grayer and tail almost wholly black.

3b Crown blue-gray, same as back. Fig. 264.

751 BLUE-GRAY GNATCATCHER. *Polióptila caerúlea caerúlea.*

Figure 264

L. 4.8; W. 2.2. Upper parts rather uniformly pale blue-gray, head a bit darker; upper tail-coverts and tail black, the latter rather broadly margined with white; under parts white. White eye-ring; bill black; eye brown.

751b WESTERN GNATCATCHER. *P. c. amoeníssima.* The gray of upper parts a bit duller than in 751.

WAXWINGS
Family *Bombycillidae*

1a Front of crown brown with whitish margin at base; under tail-coverts white; no markings of white or yellow on wings. Fig. 265.
619 CEDAR WAXWING. *Bombycílla cedrórum.*

Figure 265

L. 7.2; W. 3.7. Plumage with an exceptionally sleek and well groomed appearance. Chin, front of head and line through eye velvety black; upper parts rich grayish-brown, wings and tail grayer, the tail banded with yellow; secondaries often tipped with bright red wax plates (occasionally on tail tips also); under parts more yellowish.

2a Front of crown and under tail-coverts rufous; wings marked as pictured with white (rarely yellow). Fig. 266.
618 BOHEMIAN WAXWING. *Bombycílla gárrula pallídiceps.*

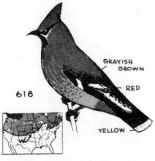

Figure 266

L. 8; W. 4.6. Rich brownish-drab above, wings and tail grayer; many of the wing feathers white tipped (sometimes yellow on primaries). The seed-shaped red sealing-wax pieces characteristic of these birds are usually present on tips of secondaries; tail tipped with yellow; breast like back, under tail-coverts rufous.

SHRIKES
Family *Laniidae*

1a Black head stripe interrupted across the forehead, lower eye lid white. Fig. 267.

621 NORTHERN SHRIKE. *Lánius boreális boreális.*

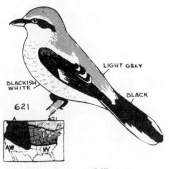

Figure 267

L. 10; W. 4.6. Plain bluish-gray above, wings and tail black; base of primaries white, making a white spot in middle of wing; outer tail feathers (occasionally all) white tipped; forehead whitish; lores gray; under parts white often finely barred with black; lower mandible pale at base.

621a NORTHWESTERN SHRIKE. *L. b. invíctus.*

1b Black head-stripe not continuous across forehead; under eyelid not white. Smaller than 1a. Fig. 268.

622 LOGGERHEAD SHRIKE. *Lánius ludoviciánus ludoviciánus.*

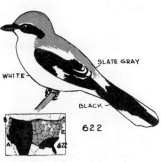

Figure 268

L. 9; W. 3.8. Plain slate-gray above, darker on head; wings and tail black, primaries white at base, secondaries white tipped; tail wholly or in part tipped with white; lores black; front of forehead with narrow black line at base of bill; under parts white, with occasional tinges of gray.

622a WHITE-RUMPED SHRIKE. *L. l. excubitorídes.* Paler above; upper tail-coverts white, more white on wings, and whiter below.

622b CALIFORNIA SHRIKE. *L. l. gámbeli.* Duller gray above with fairly white upper tail-coverts; chest often with obscure wavy bars.

622e MIGRANT SHRIKE. *L. l. mígrans.* Tail relatively short, breast white; definitely gray above.

117

VIREOS
Family *Vireonidae*

1a With conspicuous bars on wings, white or yellowish. 6

1b Wing-bars inconspicuous or not at all. 2

2a With one or two indistinct wing-bars; pale eye-ring present......3

2b Without wing-bars. 4

3a At most with but one indistinct wing-bar. Habitat dry mountain slopes. Fig. 269. **634 GRAY VIREO.** *Vireo vicínior.*

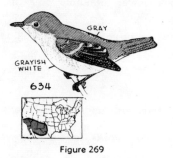

634

Figure 269

L. 5.6; W. 2.5. Upper parts plain gray with tinges of olive-green on rump, wings and tail darker; lores pale gray or whitish; under parts dull white somewhat grayer at front; bill bluish-gray; eyes brown.

The Vireos are sometimes known as "Greenlets". Their food consists very largely of small caterpillars and other insects taken from the leaves of shrubs and trees. They thus play a most valuable role.

3b With either one or two indistinct wing-bars. Habitat, shrubs and trees along prairie streams. Fig. 270.

633 BELL'S VIREO. *Vireo bélli bélli.*

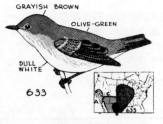

633

Figure 270

L. 4.9; W. 2.2. Upper parts olive-green, crown and back of neck grayish-brown; wings and tail deeper grayish-brown; eye-ring narrow and interrupted at front and back of eye; under parts dull white often tinged with buffy or yellowish; under tail-coverts sulphur-yellow.

633a LEAST VIREO. *V. b. pusíllus.* More grayish above; tail longer.

633b TEXAS VIREO. *V. b. médius.* Sides and flanks paler; under tail-coverts yellowish-white.

633c ARIZONA VIREO. *V. b. arizónae.* Paler than Bell's Vireo but not so pale as the Least Vireo.

4a Under parts white. 5

4b Under parts yellowish. Fig. 271.

626 PHILADELPHIA VIREO. *Vireo philadélphicus.*

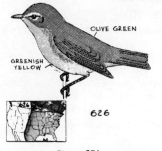

OLIVE GREEN

GREENISH YELLOW

626

Figure 271

L. 4.8; W. 2.6. Upper parts olive-green, the crown more grayish; whitish line over eye; entire under parts pale greenish-yellow.

It resembles the Red-eyed Vireo in habits and song. The nest is usually built in the forked branches of a small tree. It lays 4 speckled eggs.

5a Upper parts uniformly ashy-olive-green, sides yellowish; head markings inconspicuous. Fig. 272.

627 EASTERN WARBLING VIREO. *Vireo gílvus gílvus.*

OLIVE GREEN

WHITE

YELLOWISH

627

Figure 272

L. 5.8; W. 2.8. Ashy-olive-green above, wings, and tail darker; under parts white, yellowish tinged on sides.

627a WESTERN WARBLING VIREO. *V. g. swaínsoni.* Somewhat darker and smaller, with relatively smaller bill.

As the name indicates, the song of these birds is a long continuous warble. They frequent the tree tops and seem to prefer elms.

5b Crown gray, back olive, sides not yellowish; conspicuous line over eye, bordered above with black. Fig. 273.

624 RED-EYED VIREO. *Vireo oliváceus.*

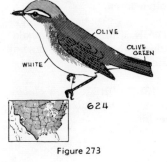

OLIVE

OLIVE GREEN

WHITE

624

Figure 273

L. 6.2; W. 3.2. Wings and tail light olive-green; under parts pure white; bill grayish; eyes dark red; brown in young birds.

This is in many regions the most common Vireo. Its deliberate song often with rising inflection has won it the title "Preacher". It sings most of the entire day.

119

6a Crown and face black. Fig. 274.
630 BLACK-CAPPED VIREO. *Víreo atricapíllus.*

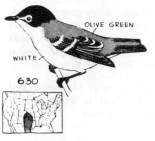

Figure 274

L. 4.6; W. 2.2. Head as pictured black (sometimes slaty); lores and eye-rings, white; back, scapulars, lesser wing-coverts and upper tail-coverts olive-green; wings and tail dull black edged with olive-green to yellow and white; wing-bars pale yellow; under parts white turning to yellowish-olive on sides and flanks; bill grayish-blue; eyes reddish brown.

6b Not as in 6a. 7

7a Top and sides of head bluish-gray; lores and eye-rings prominently white. Fig. 275.
629 BLUE-HEADED VIREO. *Víreo solitárius solitárius.*

L. 5.6; W. 3. Back olive-green; wing-bars and margins of tertials white; under parts whitish, sides greenish-yellow.

629a CASSIN'S VIREO. *V. s. cássini.* Somewhat smaller with much smaller bill.

629b PLUMBEUS VIREO. *V. s. plúmbeus.* Back scapulars and rump gray instead of olive-green.

629c MOUNTAIN VIREO. *V. s. altícola.* Largest of the subspecies; somewhat gray on back.

629d SAN LUCUS VIREO. *V. s. lucas ánus.* Smallest of the subspecies but with a large bill.

Figure 275

7b Head not bluish. 8

8a Throat and breast bright yellow. Fig. 276.
628 YELLOW-THROATED VIREO. *Vireo flávifrons.*

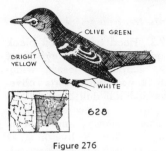

L. 6; W. 3. Bright olive-green above, becoming grayer on rump; wing bars white; tertials edged with white; lores and eye-ring yellow; throat and breast brilliant yellow, belly white.

It lays 3-4 scatteringly black-specked white eggs. The nest is built in the forked branches of a tree.

Figure 276

8b Throat and breast not yellow. 9

9a Eye-ring interrupted at top of eye; under parts olive-buff or olive-yellow. Fig. 277.
632 HUTTON'S VIREO. *Vireo húttoni húttoni.*

L. 4.6; W. 2.4. Upper parts plain olive; wings and tail dusky, the feathers edged with pale yellowish olive; wing-bands olive-buff or olive-yellow. Under part olive-buff, paler on belly and under tail-coverts; bill horn color; eyes brown.

632a STEPHEN'S VIREO. *V. h. stephensi.* Paler throughout, yellowish beneath.

632d FRAZAR'S VIREO. *V. h. cognátus.* Like 632a but without tinge of yellowish.

Figure 277

9b Under parts whitish; eye-rings yellow not interrupted. Fig. 278.
631 WHITE-EYED VIREO. *Vireo gríseus gríseus.*

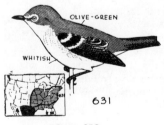

L. 5.3; W. 2.4. Bright olive-green above, wing-bars yellowish; tertials with whitish margins; lores and eye-ring yellow; throat and belly white; breast and sides washed with greenish-yellow; eyes white (browish in young birds).

631c RIO GRANDE VIREO. *V. g. micrus.* Smaller than the preceeding.

Figure 278

WOOD WARBLERS
Family *Compsothlypidae*

1a Wholly black and white (except possible faint tinges of color)....2

1b With patches of color. 4

2a Head, back and under parts striped black and white. Fig. 279.
636 BLACK AND WHITE WARBLER. *Mniotilta vária.*

636

Figure 279

L. 5.5; W. 2.7. ♂ Ear coverts black, crown, back and breast striped; no yellow, orange or red. ♀ Similar but less streaked on under parts and sides with tinges of brownish.

This little bird is very much of a creeper by habit, climbing around over the larger limbs of trees as well as the smaller branches.

2b Top of head black; mid-breast and belly white. 3

3a Crown black; throat and face under eye white; faintly tinged with olive, more so in autumn. Fig. 280.
661 BLACK-POLL WARBLER. *Dendroíca striáta.*

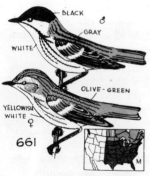

BLACK ♂
GRAY
WHITE
OLIVE-GREEN
YELLOWISH WHITE ♀
661

Figure 280

L. 5; W. 2.5. ♂ *Spring and summer.* Head above eye wholly black; back of neck streaked; face white, upper parts lightly tinger with olive or brown. ♀ *Spring and summer.* Grayish-olive-green above with blackish streaks on rump, wings and tail; under tail-coverts white as in male. Young birds and adults in autumn and winter are rather generally olive-green, somewhat obscurely striped, the young more yellowish.

3b Middle of crown black; prominent white streak over eye with black patch below eye; throat black. (♂). Fig. 281.

    665 BLACK-THROATED GRAY WARBLER. *Dendroíca nigréscens.*

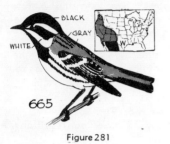

Figure 281

L. 4.5; W. 2.4. ♂ and ♀ similar. *Spring and summer.* Head as in key; with a small yellow spot in front of eye. Back wings and tail gray marked with black and white; under parts white, sides striped. *Fall.* Similar but more brownish. Young birds similar to adults but sometimes with less black.

4a With definite markings of red or vermilion. ...:...............5

4b Without red or vermilion marks. 9

5a Head and back wholly black. 6

5b Head and back not entirely black. (See also Fig. 286 which is marked with brownish-red). 7

6a Sides of breast, band on wings and spots on tail as pictured, red-orange, sometimes lighter; these marks yellowish on ♀. Fig. 282.

    687 AMERICAN REDSTART. *Setóphaga rutic̓illa.*

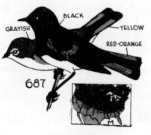

Figure 282

L. 4.9; W. 2.6. ♂ *Spring.* As in key. *Fall.* Back sometimes brownish with some white on throat and breast. ♀ Crown and cheeks gray; back olive-green; marked with yellow where ♂ has red-orange. Young male similar to ♀ but with some black on upper breast. The males seem to be aware of their beauty and are continually showing themselves to the best advantage by spreading their tail and wings and doing much strutting.

6b Breast red; white on belly, wings and tail as pictured. Fig. 283.
688 PAINTED REDSTART. *Setóphaga pícta pícta.*

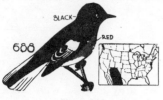

L. 4.9; W. 2.8. Sexes alike. Shining black above. See key and picture for other markings. Young birds become like adults the first fall.

This very attractive bird inhabits the high mountains of its marked region. It has no red on the face.

Figure 283

7a Crown black; forehead, throat and breast red. Fig. 284.
690 RED-FACED WARBLER. *Cardellína rúbrifrons.*

L. 5; W. 2.7. Sexes similar, female a bit duller in color. Bright red area on face and breast and white on nape, as pictured. Back, tail and wings gray; rump whitish often tinged with red. In fall the nape and rump are often more definitely tinged with red. Young rather similar to adults.

Figure 284

7b Not as in 7a. 8

8a Pretty much wholly yellow; streaks of red dots on breast (♂), very obscure in ♀; wings and tail darker.
YELLOW WARBLER. See Fig. 294.

8b Bluish above; more or less red or reddish on upper breast.
PARULA WARBLER AND SENNETT'S WARBLER. See Fig. 317.

9a With some areas colored yellow, orange, bright red or brown...10

9b Without any areas colored yellow, orange, bright red or brown...47

10a Crown of head or face in part at least, yellow, orange or bright-reddish brown. 11

10b Crown and face without any yellow, orange or bright red-brown except there may be colored eye-rings (some markings elsewhere definitely of at least one of these colors). 36

11a Crown partly orange. (See also Figs. 288 and 314)............12

11b Crown or face reddish-brown. 13

11c Yellow at least somewhere on face or top of head. 18

12a Throat and part of face orange also; crown in part black. Fig. 285.
662 BLACKBURNIAN WARBLER. *Dendroíca fúsca.*

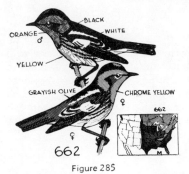

Figure 285

L. 5.3; W. 2.7. ♂ Head and throat as pictured, black and orange, rest of bird black, white and gray as pictured. ♀ Marked similar to ♂ but with paler orange. Young birds of both sexes resemble the adult ♀ but with pale yellow or buffy instead of orange.

12b Throat white; crown orange-brown margined with black. Fig. 286.
674 OVEN-BIRD. *Seiúrus aurocapíllus.*

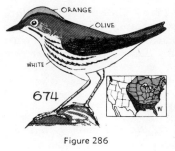

Figure 286

L. 6.2; W. 3. Sexes similar. Center of crown brownish-orange or ochraceous-buff bordered at sides with black lines; otherwise brownish olive-green above; under parts white with blackish streaks on sides.

This woods bird lives much on the ground where it builds its nest, a covered affair among the leaves with its opening at one side. The call or song is a loud, clear *"teacher, teacher, teacher."*

13a Prominent black patch surrounding or back of eye. 14

13b Without black patch back of eye. 15

14a Crown, nape, breast and sides reddish-chestnut; side of neck with buffy spot. Fig. 287.
660 BAY-BREASTED WARBLER. *Dendroíca castánea.*

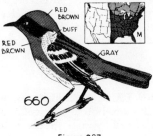

Figure 287

L. 5.6; W. 3. *Spring.* ♂ Back brownish streaked with black; belly and lower breast buffy-white. ♀ Similar to ♂ except head being somewhat marked with olive and blackish. *Fall.* Both sexes and young birds, bright olive-green above with faint streaks of black, under parts white with tinges of buff.

14b Head, throat, neck and breast orange-brown. Fig. 288.

651 OLIVE WARBLER. *Peucédramus oliváceus.*

Figure 288

L. 5; W. 3. ♂ Spring. Back grayish-olive-green; tail black; wings black with prominent white markings. Duller in fall. ♀ Spring. Olive-yellow replaces the orange-brown of ♂. Young ♂ much like adult ♀ the second spring. In fall like the young ♀ in being grayer and paler than adult ·♀.

15a With red-brown patch on face. Fig. 289.

650 CAPE MAY WARBLER. *Dendroíca tigŕina.*

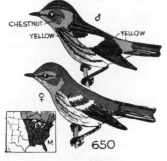

Figure 289

L.· 5; W. 2.6; ♂ Crown blackish; face red-brown bordered below with large yellow patch; rump and under parts yellow, the latter with dark stripes; large spot on wing-coverts white. ♀ Olive-green above with line over eye, streak on neck and two wing-bars and rump yellowish.

Young birds are like the ♀ but the yellow parts whitish.

15b Without red-brown patch on face. 16
16a Without wing-bars; back and wings blue-gray. 17
16b With wing-bars; yellow stripe over eye. Fig. 290.

672a YELLOW PALM WARBLER. *Dendroíca palmárum hypochrýsea.*

Figure 290

L. 5.5; W. 2.6. Crown chestnut; back brownish-olive-green; eye-ring and line over eye yellow; under parts bright yellow, streaked with chestnut on sides, breast and sides of throat. Young birds and winter adults with crown obscured and yellow over eye and on under parts more subdued. Wags tail all the while.

672 WESTERN PALM WARBLER. *D. p. palmárum.* Similar but lighter colored. Winter adults and young birds with white eye-ring.

126

17a Rump red-brown; throat and breast white. Fig. 291.
643 LUCY'S WARBLER. *Vermívora lúciae.*

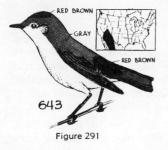

643

Figure 291

L. 4; W. 2.3. ♂ *Spring*. Crown and rump chestnut; back and wings blue-gray, without bars; tail darker; under parts whitish. *Fall*. Somewhat brownish. ♀ Paler than ♂. Young largely pale gray.

This very active little bird lives in the desert.

17b Rump yellow; part of breast and throat yellowish. Fig. 292.
644 VIRGINIA'S WARBLER. *Vermívora virgíniae.*

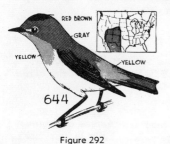

644

Figure 292

L. 4.3; W. 2.4. ♂ *Spring*. Crown chestnut; eye-ring white; tail dark with marginal feathers partly white; throat and breast in part pale yellow; belly white; under tail-coverts yellowish. ♀ Similar to ♂ but paler in color. It resembles the preceeding but is found on wooded mountain sides.

18a Entire head yellow. 19

18b Head not wholly yellow. 21

19a Throat yellow. 20

19b Throat black. Fig. 293.
669 HERMIT WARBLER. *Dendroíca occidentális.*

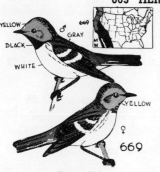

669

Figure 293

L. 4.8. W. 1.6. ♂ Head yellow, throat black as pictured; upper parts blackish; breast, belly and sides white, the latter occasionally with a few streaks. ♀ Similar to male but with less yellow on head.

Both sexes and the young are somewhat olive above, in the fall.

20a Sides and breast more or less streaked with red. Fig. 294.
    652 EASTERN YELLOW WARBLER. *Dendroíca aestíva aestíva.*

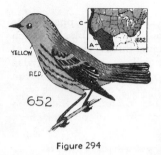

L. 5.1; W. 2.4. ♂ Head and under parts bright yellow, the latter streaked with reddish; upper parts greenish-yellow, the wings and tail darkened with blackish. ♀ More olive-green above, bright yellow beneath. Young birds resemble the ♀.

652a SONORA YELLOW WARBLER. *D. a. sonoróna.* ♂ Paler above with back more yellow. ♀ grayer.

652c CALIFORNIA YELLOW WARBLER. *D. a. brewsteri.* Smallest of the three; lighter yellow than 652.

Figure 294

20b No markings on breast; wings grayish, without bars. Fig. 295.
    637 PROTHONOTARY WARBLER. *Prothonotária cítrea.*

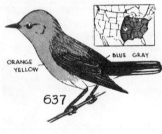

L. 5.5; W. 2.9. ♂ Entire head and breast bright orange-yellow, belly lighter; back greenish-yellow, wings and tail bluish-ash. ♀ Paler yellow, belly with some whitish.
Unlike many of the warblers that nest in the far north, this bird is more southern and nests wholly within the United States. It is conspicuous and readily recognized.

Figure 295

21a Yellow on some part of face, but not at all on forehead or crown.
   28

21b Forehead or crown marked with yellow. 22

22a Crown wholly or in part yellow bordered in front by black or gray forehead. 23

22b Forehead and sometimes part of the crown yellow. 24

23a Throat yellow. (See Figs. 285 and 288 which might be placed here by mistake). Fig. 296.

656 AUDUBON'S WARBLER. *Dendroíca aúbuboni aúduboni.*

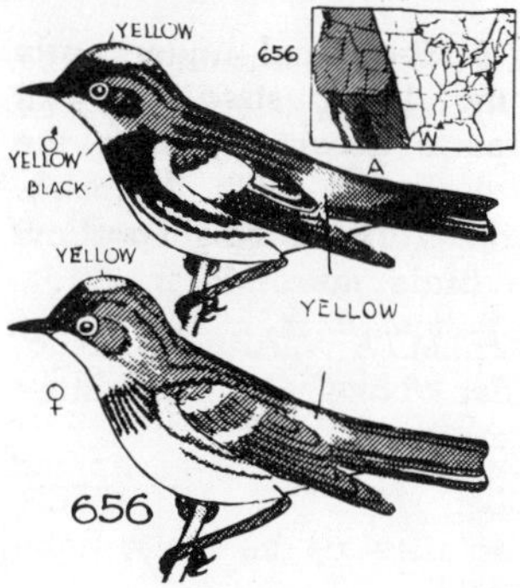

L. 5.3; W. 3. ♂ *Spring.* Upper parts bluish-gray marked with black; patch on crown, rump, throat and sides of breast bright yellow; breast otherwise black, belly white; wings with large white areas. *Fall.* More brownish with yellow markings duller. ♀ Similar to fall ♂. Young birds till browner than fall adults.

656a BLACK-FRONTED WARBLER. *D. a. nígrifrons.* Larger and with black streaks broader.

Figure 296

23b Throat white. Fig. 297.

655 MYRTLE WARBLER. *Dendroíca coronáta.*

L. 5.7; W. 2.9. ♂ Crown, rump and sides of breast bright yellow; upper parts black streaked on bluish-gray; wings with two white bars; breast black; belly white, striped with black as pictured. ♀ Paler and with less black. Young and fall adults with tinges of brown especially on the yellow areas.

Figure 297

24a Front of throat wholly white. Fig. 298.

659 CHESTNUT-SIDED WARBLER. *Dendroíca pensylvánica.*

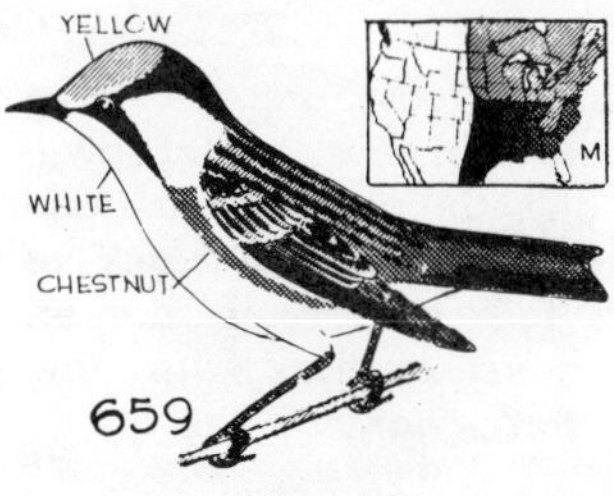

L. 5.2; W. 2.5. ♂ Forehead and crown yellow; back olive-green streaked with black; small marks around eye black; throat and under parts white; sides chestnut. ♀ Similar but duller. Fall adults and young birds yellowish-green above; under parts pure white; occasional spots of chestnut showing on sides.

Figure 298

24b Throat not wholly white. 25

25a Throat wholly yellow. 26

25b Throat at least in part black. 27

26a Wings bluish with two white bars; black mark through eyes. Fig. 299.   **641 BLUE-WINGED WARBLER.** *Vermívora pínus.*

L. 4.8; W. 2.4. ♂ Forehead, part of crown and entire under parts bright yellow; face yellow with a black line through eye; back olive-green, wings and tail bluish-gray. ♀ Somewhat duller with yellow on top of head limited to the forehead.

Figure 299

26b Wings olive-green without wing-bars; no mark through eye. Fig. 300.   **685 WILSON'S WARBLER.** *Wilsónia pusílla pusílla.*

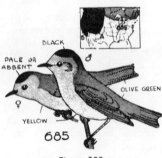

L. 5; W. 2.2. ♂ Forehead, face and under parts bright yellow; crown black; back, wings and tail bright olive-green. ♀ Crown usually olive-green instead of black.

685a NORTHERN PILEOLATED WARBLER. *W. p. pileoláta.* Forehead orange, and color of other yellow parts, deeper.

685b GOLDEN PILEOLATED WARBLER. *W. p. chryséola.* Smaller than either of the other two with still deeper yellow than 685a.

Figure 300

27a Breast and belly yellow, no wing-bars. 28

27b Breast and belly white; wing-bars yellow. Fig. 301.   **642 GOLDEN-WINGED WARBLER.** *Vermívora chrysóptera.*

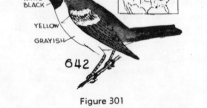

L. 5.1; W. 2.5. ♂ Forehead and front of crown and wing-bars, bright yellow; face and throat black as pictured; upper parts bluish-gray the wings and tail somewhat darker. The black areas of the ♂ grayish and lighter throughout on the ♀.

Figure 301

28a Black crown connected with black throat, as pictured. Fig. 302.
684 HOODED WARBLER. Wilsónia citrína.

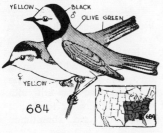

Figure 302

L. 5.7; W. 2.6. ♂ Forehead, face and under parts bright yellow; upper parts, wings and tail olíve-green. ♀ Black hood almost wholly absent; generally paler than male. Young ♂ like adult ♂ but with some yellow tips on black feathers.

28b Black crown not connecting with black of throat. Fig. 303.
640 BACHMAN'S WARBLER. Vermívora báchmani.

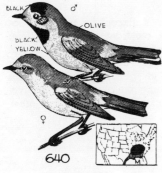

Figure 303

L. 4.3; W. 2.4. ♂ Forehead, lesser wing-coverts and under parts yellow; crown in part black; nape bluish-gray, back and rump bright olive-green; tail grayish with white markings. ♀ Crown gray; black throat patch of male absent; under parts lighter than in ♂, often whitish. Young ♂ with smaller throat patch than adult ♂.

31b Breast yellow. Fig. 304.

668 TOWNSEND'S WARBLER. *Dendroíca townsendi.*

Figure 304

L. 5; W. 2.6. ♂ Head and throat bright yellow and black as pictured; (In fall this black area is partly masked with olive-green); breast yellow with black stripes on sides, belly white; back, wings, and tail gray and blackish; the wings with two bars and the tail with markings of white. ♀ Similar to ♂ but with black areas dull and sometimes olive-green.

32a Crown and line through eye black. Fig. 305.

666 GOLDEN-CHEEKED WARBLER. *Dendroíca chrysoparia.*

Figure 305

L. 5; W. 2.5. ♂ Except for face and obscure streak on front of head, yellow; this bird is wholly black and and white. ♀ Olive-green above streaked with black and in general more grayish than ♂. Young birds still lighter olive-green on back and lighter gray on other dark parts.

32b Crown and line through eye olive-green. Fig. 306.

667 BLACK-THROATED GREEN WARBLER. *Dendroíca vírens vírens.*

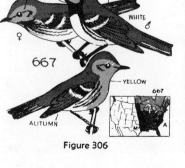

Figure 306

L. 5.1; W. 2.5. ♂ Upper parts bright olive-green, sometimes with black spotting on back; wings and tail darker, marked with white; face as pictured bright yellow; throat, upper breast and stripes on sides black; belly whitish. ♀ Similar but throat and breast mixed with yellow. Young birds still more yellowish.

667a WAYNE'S WARBLER. *D. v. waýnei.*

33a Bluish-gray above; yellow spot under eye; belly and wing-bars white. Fig. 307.

664 GRACE'S WARBLER. *Dendroíca gráciae gráciae.*

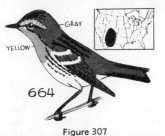

L. 5; W. 2.6. ♂ Upper parts bluish-gray, with white and black markings; parts of face as pictured, and throat and sides yellow, the latter with streaks of black; belly white. ♀ Somewhat browner above with yellow less bright.

Figure 307

33b Bright olive-green above; yellow streak under eye; belly and wing-bars yellow. (♀ of Fig. 293 might fall here). Fig. 308.

673 NORTHERN PRAIRIE WARBLER. *Dendroíca díscolor díscolor.*

L. 4.8; W. 2.2. ♂ Back striped or spotted with reddish-chestnut; tail marked with white at tip. ♀ With less or no reddish-marks on back.

673a FLORIDA PRAIRIE WARBLER. *D. d. cóllinsi.*

Figure 308

34a Throat yellow. 35

34b Throat white or whitish. 48

35a Face with prominent black patch running diagonally across eye with gray border behind. (NORTHERN YELLOW-THROAT might seem to come here) Turn to Fig. 311.

35b Without black patch on face; 2 white wing-bars. (See also Figs. 287 ♀, 289 and 328; if in fall plumage, Fig. 280; if the bird has a reddish-brown crown, Fig. 290. If with yellow eye-rings or "specaacles" go to 36.) Fig. 309.

671 NORTHERN PINE WARBLER. *Dendroíca pínus pínus.*

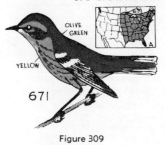

L. 5.5; W. 2.8. ♂ Olive-green above, often with ashy tinge; under parts bright yellow; lower belly and under tail-coverts white; sides often with dark streaks. ♀ Similar but lighter.

671a FLORIDA PINE WARBLER. *D. p. flórida.*

Figure 309

133

36a Throat and breast plain yellow (unmarked). 37

36b Throat and breast of at least two colors. 41

37a Conspicuous black patch around or under eye. 38

37b No such black marking. 39

38a With irregular black patch below eye and on neck as pictured. Fig. 310. 577 KENTUCKY WARBLER. Oporórnis formósus.

L. 5.4; W. 2.6. ♂ Upper parts olive green with black on side of head as pictured; eye-ring and line to bill yellow; crown grayish; under parts bright yellow. ♀ Similar to ♂ but black markings less definite.

Figure 310

38b Diagonal black patch covering eye, bordered behind by whitish line. Fig. 311.

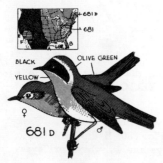

681d NORTHERN YELLOW-THROAT. Geóthlypis tríchas brachidáctyla.

L. 5.4; W. 2.2. ♂ Upper parts olive-green; head marked with black and grayish white as pictured; throat and breast bright yellow becoming whitish on belly. ♀ Without black and gray markings. Its "witchity-witchity-witch" call is highly characteristic.

681 MARYLAND YELLOW-THROAT. G. t. tríchas.

681a WESTERN YELLOW-THROAT. G. t. occidentális. The largest and most richly colored subspecies; the underparts sometimes orange.

681b FLORIDA YELLOW-THROAT. G. t. ignóta. Somewhat darker than 681d with black patch wider.

681e SALT MARSH YELLOW-THROAT. G. t. sinuósa. Smaller with gray margin line narrow.

681f TULE YELLOW-THROAT. G. t. scirpícola.

682.1 RIO GRANDE YELLOW-THROAT. Chamaéthlypis poliocéphala poliocéphala. Head slate colored with small black patch in front of eye. The bill is rather heavy and definitely curved.

Figure 311

39a Head bluish (if bars on wings see Fig. 316 ♀). Fig. 312.
645 NASHVILLE WARBLER. *Vermívora ruticapílla ruticapílla.*

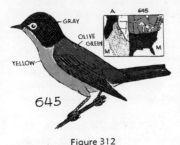

L. 4.8; W. 2.3. Top and sides of head bluish-gray with an obscure chestnut patch on the crown; back, wings and tail olive-green; under parts bright yellow becoming lighter on belly.

645a CALAVERAS WARBLER. *V. r. rídgwayi.* Deeper yellow with brighter rump.

Figure 312

39b Head not bluish. **40**

40a Large for a warbler; eye-ring and line to bill white; belly white. Fig. 313.   683 YELLOW-BREASTED CHAT. *Ictéria vírens vírens.*

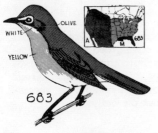

L. 7.5; W. 3. Upper parts olive-green; eye-ring and line to bill white; throat, breast and upper belly bright yellow; lower belly whitish; sides grayish. Both sexes marked the same.

683a LONG-TAILED CHAT. *I. v. longicaúda.* Wings and tail longer with slimmer bill; yellow deeper and upper parts grayer.

Figure 313

40b Smaller; under parts greenish yellow; base of crown-feathers rusty-orange. Fig. 314.
646 ORANGE-CROWNED WARBLER. *Vermívora celáta celáta.*

L. 5; W. 2.5. Ashy-olive-green above; crown feathers rusty-orange at base not much apparent; eye-ring yellow; under parts greenish-yellow streaked obscurely with darker. Immature birds have a white eye-ring.

646a LUTESCENT WARBLER. *V. c. lutéscens.* Smaller and more definitely yellow, even above. Breeds in Alaska; migrates into our western states.

646b DUSKY WARBLER. *V. c. sórdida.* The size of 646a but darker; with plainer streaks on under parts. Occasionally in S. W. California.

Figure 314

41a Throat yellow. **43**
41b Throat dark; head bluish. **42**
42a Upper breast with large black spot (♂) (drab in ♀). No eye-ring.
    Fig. 315.   **679 MOURNING WARBLER.** *Oporórnis philadélphia.*

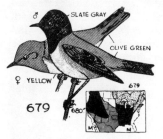

L. 5.6; W. 2.6. ♂ Bluish-gray on head, neck and throat; upper breast black; back, wings and tail olive-green, unmarked; belly yellow. ♀ and young lighter; breast grayish and throat more nearly white.

680 MACGILLIVRAY'S WARBLER. O. *tólmiei.* Lower side of eye-ring white; black on breast more slaty.

Figure 315

42b Upper breast colored similar to head and throat (♂), grayish-brown, (♀); eye-ring white. Fig. 316.
                678 CONNECTICUT WARBLER. *Oporórnis ágilis.*

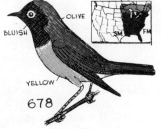

L. 5.4; W. 2.9. ♂ Bluish-gray on head, neck and breast; throat lighter; back, wings and tail olive-green without markings; belly yellow turning to olive-green on sides. ♀ *and young.* Throat and breast light grayish-brown becoming pale yellow on belly.

Figure 316

43a Head, wings and tail light blue or bluish-gray. Fig. 317.
          648a NORTHERN PARULA WARBLER.
            Compsóthlypis americána pusílla.

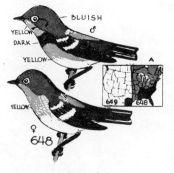

L. 4.7; W. 2.4. ♂ Yellowish-green spot on middle of back; lores black. Two wing-bars and marking at tip of tail white; throat yellow; yellow breast crossed with bands of reddish, bluish or blackish; belly white; sides sometimes with streak of rufous. ♀ Similar but sometimes lacking parts or all of band markings on breast.

648 SOUTHERN PARULA WARBLER. *C. a. americána.* Somewhat larger yellow areas and less black on lores.

649 SENNETT'S WARBLER. *C. pitiayúmi nigrilóra.* Quite similar to 648 but somewhat brighter tinted and with black on cheeks.

Figure 317

43b Not as in 43a. **44**

   663 YELLOW-THROATED WARBLER. *Dendroíca domínica domínica.*

44a Breast and belly white striped with black. Fig. 318.

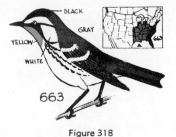

663

Figure 318

L. 5.3; W. 2.6. ♂ Upper parts gray; forehead and crown blackish; line over eye white (yellow at front); throat and neck marked with yellow, black and white as pictured; wing-bars white. ♀ *and young.* Similar but with less black on head, throat and neck.

663a SYCAMORE WARBLER. *D. d. albilora.* Line from bill to eye white instead of yellow.

44b Breast and belly yellow. **45**

45a Without prominent black and white markings. . . . .·. . .**46**

45b Head, wings and tail conspicuously marked with black and white. Fig. 319.   **657 MAGNOLIA WARBLER.** *Dendroíca magnólia.*

657

Figure 319

L. 5.1; W. 2.3. ♂ Bluish-gray above heavily marked with white, black and yellow as pictured. ♀ Similar but paler and duller colored. Young birds and adults in the fall with less black and more ashy-gray.

This is one of the most beautiful Warblers. The males like the male Redstarts are great "show-offs" and strut around in the trees and bushes as they feed.

46a Without wing-bars; upper breast striped. Fig. 320.
        686 CANADA WARBLER. *Wilsónia canadénsis.*

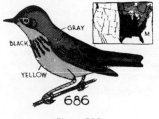

686

Figure 320

L. 5.6; W. 2.5. ♂ Upper parts gray, without marks on wings or tail; eye-ring and line to bill and under parts yellow, the breast with a "necklace" of black streaks or spots; crown spotted with black. ♀ and young somewhat paler without black on head.

46b Two white wing-bars; lores black. Fig. 321.
670 KIRTLAND'S WARBLER. Dendroíca kírtlandi.

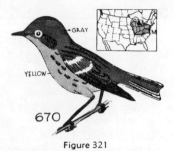

Figure 321

L. 5.8; W. 2.8. ♂ Back ashy-brown with black markings; head blue-gray with black spots on top and a patch on face; under parts yellow, streaked on sides with blackish. ♀ Similar but duller; face markings grayish.

47a Under parts rather uniformly one color, white or whitish. 48

47b Under parts at least two colors. 50

48a Head and upper parts brownish-olive-green. 49

48b Head gray. Fig. 322.
647 TENNESSEE WARBLER. Vermívora peregrína.

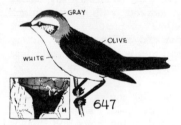

Figure 322

L. 5; W. 2.6. ♂ Back, wings and tail bright olive-green without wing-bars; head plainly gray; under parts wholly white, sometimes with yellowish tinge. ♀ and young. More greenish above especially on head and yellowish below.

49a Top of head striped black on buffy. Fig. 323.
639 WORM-EATING WARBLER. Helmítheros vermívorus.

Figure 323

L. 5.5; W. 2.8. Back, tail and wings olive-green unmarked with white; head buffy with black streak from eye to bill and two black streaks on crown; under parts whitish tinged with cream or buff. Nests on the ground in the woods.

49b Crown brownish without stripes except whitish line over eye.
(See also ♀ Fig. 325). Fig. 324.
638 SWAINSON'S WARBLER. *Limnóthlypis swaínsoni.*

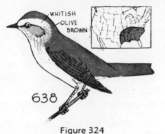

Figure 324

L. 5; W. 2.8. Back, wings and tail grayish olive-brown without any white markings; crown cinnamon-brownish; line over eye whitish; under parts white tinged with yellow or cream somewhat darker on sides. Nests in low bushes.

50a Upper parts olive-brown; breast with several stripes. 52

50b Blue or bluish-gray above. 51

51a Throat black, single white spot on wing. Fig. 325.
654 BLACK-THROATED BLUE WARBLER.
Dendroíca caeruléscens caeruléscens.

Figure 325

L. 5.3; W. 2.5. ♂ Upper parts grayish-blue or bluish; throat breast and sides black, as pictured. ♀ Olive-green above often tinged with blue; under parts pale buffy-yellow.

654a CAIRN'S WARBLER. *D. c. caírnsi.* Back at least spotted with black, sometimes almost wholly black.

51b Throat white; wing with 2 white bars. Fig. 326.
658 CERULEAN WARBLER. *Dendroíca cerúlea.*

Figure 326

L. 4.5; W. 2.7. ♂ Bright cerulean blue above, with streaks of black on back and on sides of head; stripe on sides and band across breast as pictured, bluish-black. ♀ Bluish-olive-green above, wings and tail marked with blue. Nest in low bushes.

139

52a Eye-stripe pure white, ground color of under parts usually white, sometimes tinged with cream; no streaks on throat. Fig. 327.

676 LOUISIANA WATER-THRUSH. *Seiúrus motacílla.*

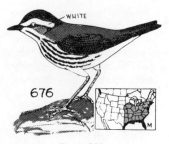

Figure 327

L. 6.3; W. 3.2. Head, back, tail and wings olive-brown; under parts white or pale cream and streaked with blackish except on throat and mid-belly.

This shy bird prefers to build its nest along a rocky woodland stream.

52b Eye-stripe buffy; under parts tinged with sulphur yellow; streaks on throat. Fig. 328.

675 NORTHERN WATER-THRUSH. *Seiúrus noveboracénsis noveboracénsis.*

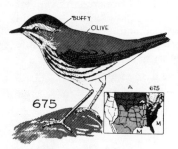

Figure 328

L. 6; W. 3. Olive-brown above without markings on wings or tail; under parts white with sulphur yellow tinge; black streaking includes throat as well as rest of under parts.

675a GRINNELL'S WATER-THRUSH. *S. n. notábilis.* Larger and darker above; under parts whiter.

MEADOWLARKS, BLACKBIRDS AND ORIOLES
Family *Icteridae*

1a Belly and part or all of breast black (often with metallic sheen.) .2

1b Belly and lower breast other then black. 8

2a Except for metallic sheen wholly black. 3

2b Prominently marked with colors other than black. 5

3a Plumage uniformly bluish-black (feathers sometimes tipped with brown or buff.) All tail feathers nearly equal in length. Fig. 329.

509 RUSTY BLACKBIRD. *Eúphagus carolínus.*

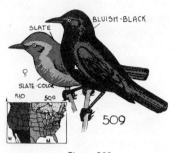

Figure 329

L. 9.5; W. 4.6. ♂ Wholly glossy blue-black at nesting time; in winter and with young males the feathers of upper parts are tipped with brown; those of underparts with buff. ♀ Slate-color, wings and tail darker, glossy; in winter reddish-brown above, buffy below.

510 BREWER'S BLACKBIRD. *E. cyanocéphalus.* Much like the above but with violet-purple iridescence on head and but scant rusty tips to winter feathers.

3b Side tail feathers shorter than middle ones, and otherwise not as in 3a. 4

4a Tail nearly half the entire length of bird. Fig. 330.

513 BOAT-TAILED GRACKLE. *Cássidix mexicánus májor.*

Figure 330

L. 16; W. 7.5. ♂ Shining bluish-black, head and breast purplish. ♀ Smaller; brownish above, dusky buff below.

513a GREAT-TAILED GRACKLE. *C. m. mexicánus.* Larger than the preceeding with tail proportionateiy larger. ♀ Noticably darker and blacker than ♀ of above.

4b Tail noticably shorter than head and body. Fig. 331.

511b BRONZED GRACKLE. *Quíscalus quíscula aéneus.*

Figure 331

L. 12; W. 5.6. ♂ Upper breast, throat, head and neck metallic blue-green to purple; back metallic bronze; wings and tail purplish; eyes yellow. ♀ Similar but duller.

511 PURPLE GRACKLE. *Q. q. quíscula.* Somewhat more purplish and feathers of back displaying iridescent bars not present in the Bronzed Grackle.

511a FLORIDA GRACKLE. *Q. q. aglaéus.* Colored much as 511b but smaller in size.

141

5a Head wholly velvety black. Wing with bright scarlet spot with buffy or whitish margin as pictured. Fig. 332.
  498 EASTERN RED-WING. *Ageláius phoeníceus phoeníceus.*

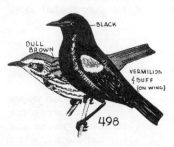

L. 9.5; W. 4.7. ♂ Lesser wing coverts scarlet or vermilion; middle wing coverts buffy or yellowish. ♀ Blackish above overtoned with brownish; much streaked buff and brownish or black below; throat marked with orange or yellow.

Thirteen subspecies have been named for our region. Two closely related species are also listed. Their differences are minor and there is some overlapping in distribution especially during migration.

498a SONORA RED-WING. *A. p. sonoriénsis.*

498b MAYNARD'S RED-WING. *A. p. floridánus.* Smaller, with long slender bill.

498c FLORIDA RED-WING. *A. p. meárnsi.*

498d THICK-BILLED RED-WING. *A. p. fórtis.*

498e SAN DIEGO RED-WING. *A. p. neutrális.*

498f NORTHWESTERN RED-WING. *A. p. caurínus.*

498g RIO GRANDE RED-WING. *A. p. megopótamus.*

498h GULF COAST RED-WING. *A. p. littorális.*

498i GIANT RED-WING. *A. p. arctólegus.*

498j NEVADA RED-WING. *A. p. nevadénsis.*

498k SAN FRANCISCO RED-WING. *A. p. mailliardórum.*

498l KERN RED-WING. *A. p. aciculátus.*

499 BICOLORED RED-WING. *A. p. califórnicus.* Wing patch wholly red.

500 TRICOLORED RED-WING. *A. trícolor.* Red patch edged with white instead of yellow.

Figure 332.

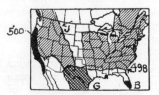

5b Head with colors other than black. 6

6a Back of head, and nape buffy; wing-coverts and rump white.
Fig. 333.   494 BOBOLINK. *Dolichónyx oryzívorus.*

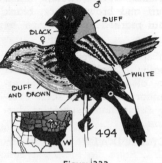

Figure 333

L. 7.3; W. 3.8. ♂ Summer plumage, black, white and buff as pictured. Early spring plumage, head rusty-brown, nape tawny, back brown and buff, under parts buffy flecked with rufous, rump and shoulders light, wings dark. (the tips wear off of these feathers to make the summer plumage, without a molt.) ♀ Summer. Buffy with stripes above of white and brown and small spots of brown below. Both sexes during fall and winter resemble the female of summer but are deeper buff. The ♂ assumes various patterns as he is in the process of his post-nuptial molt.

6b Not as in 6a. 7
7a Head and neck brown. Fig. 334.
                              495 EASTERN COWBIRD. *Molóthrus áter áter.*

L. 8; W. 4.3. ♂ Head, neck and upper breast brown, otherwise glossy black with metallic iridescence of greens and blues. ♀ Dark brownish-slate, lighter on under parts.

495a DWARF COWBIRD. *M. a. obscúrus.* Colored as above but decidedly smaller.

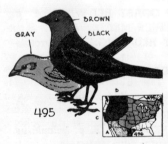

Figure 334

495b NEVADA COWBIRD. *M. a. artemísiae.*

495c CALIFORNIA COWBIRD. *M. a. californicus.*

496 RED-EYED COWBIRD. *Tangávius aéneus invulcrátus.* ♂ Head colored same as body, greenish-bronze; shades of blue and violet appear on upper tail-coverts, wings and tail. Eye red. A rather conspicuous ruff on neck in breeding season.

7b Head and neck bright yellow. Fig. 335.
497 YELLOW-HEADED BLACKBIRD. *Xanthocéphalus xanthocéphalus.*

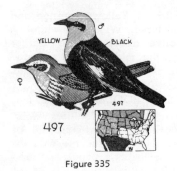

L. 10; W. 5.5. ♂ Head, neck, throat and upper breast deep yellow; some black around the mouth as pictured; wing-coverts white. ♀ Head and throat with markings of pale dull yellow; breast often marked with white; general body color gray-brown.

Figure 335

8a Belly white, streaked with black or brown, throat and breast lemon yellow marked with black; tail heavily margined with white. Fig. 336.   501 EASTERN MEADOWLARK. *Sturnélla mágna mágna.*

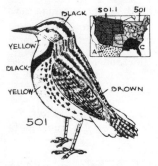

L. 10.8; W. 4.8. Top of head striped black and buff, face whitish; back and mid-tail reddish-brown, wings darker; other parts as in key.

501a RIO GRANDE MEADOWLARK. *S. m. hoópesi.* Smaller than above with deeper yellow, and with upper parts lighter.

501c SOUTHERN MEADOWLARK.*S. m. argútula.* Smaller than 501 and darker colored.

501.1 WESTERN MEADOWLARK. *S. neglécta.* Yellow of throat overflowing to cover more or less of the malar area (cheek); lighter and more gray above than 501. The difference in song is the most outstanding distinction. As a state bird it has been chosen by Kansas, Montana, Nebraska, North Dakota, Oregon and Wyoming.

Figure 336

8b Not as in 8a. 9

9a Crown black. 10

9b Crown orange, throat black. Fig. 337.

505 SENNETT'S ORIOLE. *Ícterus cucullátus sénnetti.*

L. 7.5; W. 3.3. ♂ Yellowish-orange and black as pictured. Wing-bars white. ♀ Yellowish-olive above, wings darker and dusky, the middle coverts tipped with white; dull ochre-yellow beneath, lighter on belly.

505a ARIZONA HOODED ORIOLE. *I. c. nélsoni.* ♂ Deep yellow with no orange tinge. ♀ A bit lighter in color than the above.

Figure 337

10a Head and neck wholly black. 11

10b Face orange with black line through eye and black area on chin and throat. Fig. 338.

508 BULLOCK'S ORIOLE. *Ícterus búllocki.*

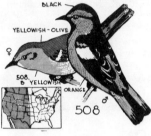

L. 8; W. 4. ♂ Markings on wing white, all other parts black or orange, as pictured. ♀ Top of head and neck yellowish-olive becoming grayer on back; tail yellowish; under parts pale buffy or yellowish; wings marked with white.

Figure 338

11a Under parts and rump brick (dark) red. Fig. 339.

506 ORCHARD ORIOLE. *Ícterus spúrius.*

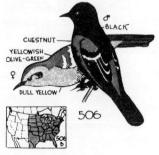

L. 7.3; W. 3.2. ♂ Wings marked with whitish; other parts black or reddish-chestnut. The winter plumage is largely tipped with buffy or fuscous with various different aspects during the molt. In its first nuptial plumage the ♂ is yellow below with black spot on throat and breast. ♀ Grayish-olive-green above; dull yellow below.

Figure 339

145

11b Under parts and rump yellow or orange. 12

12a Back (and head) black. 13

12b Back deep yellow, same as rump and under parts. Fig. 340.
    503 AUDUBON'S ORIOLE. *Ícterus melanocéphalus aúduboni.*

L. 9; W. 4. ♂ Markings on wing white; all other parts black or saffron yellow somewhat tinged with greenish. ♀ Marked much as male but duller. Size smaller.

Figure 340

13a Under parts and rump lemon yellow; all tail feathers black at tip. (See picture). Fig. 341.
    504 SCOTT'S ORIOLE. *Ícterus parisórum.*

L. 8; W. 4.2. ♂ Markings on wings white; all other parts black or deep lemon yellow. ♀ Olive-grayish above more yellowish to rear, tail yellowish-olive with middle feathers and tip of entire tail darker; under parts yellowish-olive.

Figure 341

13b Under parts and rump bright orange; only middle tail feathers black at tip, others orange-yellow (see picture). Fig. 342.
    507 BALTIMORE ORIOLE. *Ícterus gálbula.*

L. 7.5; W. 3.5. ♂ Greater wing-coverts and primaries edged with white; all other parts orange or black. ♀ Brownish or grayish-orange above; head and back mottled with black; under parts dull orange, the throat occasionally with black markings.

Figure 342

146

FEMALES AND YOUNG MALES

There is much irregularity in the markings of the females of this group which is further complicated by the young males in many cases taking the coloration of the adult males rather tardily. The following supplementary keys are offered as an attempt to help identify those forms not responding to the use of preceeding keys. These irregular individuals may usually be most easily told by their association with males of the same species.

1a Uniform slate or sooty gray. COWBIRD. Fig. 334.

1b Not wholly gray. 2

2a Some shade of olive above, not striped or spotted below. 3

2b Brown or brownish or buff with brown stripes above. 12

3a Throat black or dusky. 4

3b Throat not black or dusky. 9

4a Back without any black. 5

4b Back marked more or less with black. 7

5a Top of head black or partly so; back and rump grayish. AUDUBON'S ORIOLE. Fig. 340.

5b Top of head olive-green or yellowish. 6

6a Top of head fairly dark olive-green; under parts yellowish; tail shorter. ORCHARD ORIOLE Fig. 339.

6b Top of head light yellowish-olive-green; tail longer. SENNETT'S AND HOODED ORIOLES. Fig. 337.

7a Top of head without black streaks or spots. BULLOCK'S ORIOLE. Fig. 338.

7b Top of head wholly or partly black. 8

8a Sides of head and neck grayish, larger. SCOTT'S ORIOLE. Fig. 341.

8b Head streaked or spotted or wholly black; smaller. BALTIMORE ORIOLE. Fig. 342.

9a With streak of lighter color above eye bordered by darker area through or below eye. 10

9b Not as in 9a. SENNETT'S AND HOODED ORIOLES. Fig. 337.

10a Narrow dull line through eye with yellowish below. BULLOCK'S ORIOLE. Fig. 338.

10b Darker patch through eye fairly wide. 11

11a Brownish-gray above. BALTIMORE ORIOLE. Fig. 342.

11b Yellowish-olive above with darker patches on wing. ORCHARD ORIOLE. Fig. 339.

12a Buff with dark brown striped head, back, wings and tail and small spots on breast (female and winter male—"Reed-bird" of South.) BOBOLINK. Fig. 333.

12b Not as in 12a. 13

13a Throat dark reddish-brown like back, streak of tan or deep buff above eye (female RUSTY BLACKBIRD. Fig. 329.

13b Throat much lighter than back. 14

14a Throat and line over eye yellow. (female) YELLOW-HEADED BLACKBIRD. Fig. 335.

14b Throat and line over eye buff. (female). RED-WING. Fig. 332.

TANAGERS
Family *Thraupidae*

1a Marked at least in part with red (males in their breeding plumage). 2

1b Olive with or without black above, yellowish below. No red adult males while molting. 5

MALES

2a Under parts and rump lemon yellow. Fig. 343.
607 WESTERN TANAGER. *Piránga ludoviciána.*

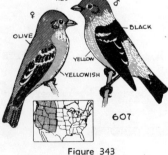
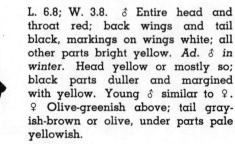

L. 6.8; W. 3.8. ♂ Entire head and throat red; back wings and tail black, markings on wings white; all other parts bright yellow. *Ad. ♂ in winter.* Head yellow or mostly so; black parts duller and margined with yellow. Young ♂ similar to ♀. ♀ Olive-greenish above; tail grayish-brown or olive, under parts pale yellowish.

Figure 343

148

2b **Without any yellow.** 3

3a **Wings and tail black; head and body scarlet. Fig. 344.**
608 **SCARLET TANAGER.** *Piránga erythrómelas.*

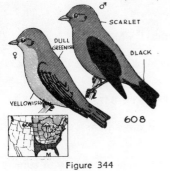

Figure 344

L. 7.3; W. 3.8. *Ad. ♂ in Summer.* Bright scarlet and black; under wing coverts white. *Ad. ♂ in Winter.* Like ♀ but with black wings and tail. *Im. ♂ Winter.* Like ♀ but with wing-coverts black. *Ad. ♀.* Light olive-green above, wings and tail fuscous, margined with greenish; greenish-yellow beneath.

3b **Wholly red or reddish.** 4

4a **Underparts orange-red; upper parts dusky red; bill dark with distinct tooth at middle. (See A, Fig. 156.) Fig. 345.**
609 **HEPATIC TANAGER.** *Piránga fláva hepática.*

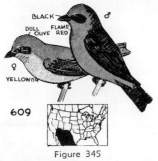

Figure 345

L. 7.2; W. 4.1. *Ad. ♂ in summer.* As in key. Duller and more brownish fall and winter. *Ad. ♀ in summer.* Upper parts olive-green to grayish-olive; under parts mainly yellow. Plumage softer and a bit brighter in fall and winter.

4b **Under parts pure vermilion; upper parts dull vermilion or rosered; bill light brown, tooth not apparent. Fig. 346.**
610 **SUMMER TANAGER.** *Piránga rúbra rúbra.*

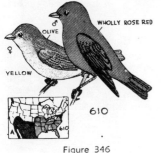

Figure 346

L. 7.6; W. 3.8. *Ad. ♂* Colors as in key. *Im. ♂ in winter.* Similar to female but more reddish. ♀ Orange-olive-green above, yellowish-orange below.

610a COOPER'S TANAGER. *P. r. coóperi.* Somewhat larger and lighter in color than the above.

FEMALES AND IMMATURES AND WINTERING MALES

5a Clear olive and yellow. 6

5b Not as above. 7

6a With wing-bars (2 yellow or 1 yellow and 1 white).
WESTERN TANAGER. Fig. 343.
Back and tail black. Ad. ♂ in winter. Back and tail not black. Ad.
♀.

6b Without wing-bars. **SCARLET TANAGER. Fig. 347.**
Wings and tail black. Ad. ♂ in winter.
Wings and tail dusky gray with edging of olive-green. Ad. ♀ and
Im. ♂.

7a Ashy-olive and pale yellow; bill dark with tooth at middle of side.
♀ **HEPATIC TANAGER. Fig. 345.**

7b Brownish-olive and buffy-yellow, bill light brown, no tooth. ♀ **SUM-
MER TANAGER AND COOPER'S TANAGER. Fig. 346.**

GROSBEAKS, FINCHES, SPARROWS AND BUNTINGS
Family *Fringillidae*

1a With evident markings of blue, bright yellow or red. 2

1b Birds without the above colors; marked with various combinations
of brown, black and white. 23

2a At least the head, back and tail blue (or bluish). (Head blue, back
not blue,—see 600 and 601.) 3

2b Not as in 2a. 5

3a Underparts blue. 4

3b Throat blue, breast and sides brown, belly whitish. **Fig. 347.**
599 LAZULI BUNTING. *Passerína amoéna.*

L. 6; W. 2.9. ♂ Head, throat and back
azure blue; wings and tail blackish with
two white wing-bars; breast tawny-
brownish extending along sides; belly
and under tail-coverts white. ♀ Grayish-brown above often with greenish-
blue tinge; breast buffy, belly whitish.

Figure 347

150

4a Indigo (greenish) blue; no wing-bars; smaller. (♂). Fig. 348.

598 INDIGO BUNTING. *Passerína cyánea.*

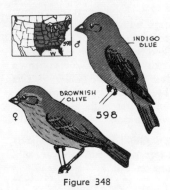

L. 5.6; W. 2.6. ♂ *Summer.* Wings and tail black, margined with blue, lores blackish. ♀ Grayish-brown above, wings and tail fuscous; under parts whitish. ♂ in winter and young birds resemble the ♀, the adult ♂ often with patches of blue.

Figure 348

4b Purplish-blue with 2 reddish-brown wing-bars; larger (♂). Fig. 349.

597 EASTERN BLUE GROSBEAK. *Guiraca caerúlea caerúlea.*

L. 7; W. 3.5. ♂ Lores and chin and wngs and tail black, the latter edged with blue. Winter males are much margined 'with rusty while year old males are mottled. ♀ Grayish-brown sometimes with some blue, wings and tail darker, under parts buffy-brown.

597a WESTERN BLUE GROSBEAK. *G. c. interfúsa.* Lighter colored with longer wings and tail.

597b CALIFORNIA BLUE GROSBEAK. *G. c. salicária.*

Figure 349

5a With areas of bright yellow. (for very small yellow markings see Figs. 392 and 397). 6

5b Marked at least in part with red. 11

6a Chin and entire under parts yellow. 7

6b Not all of chin and under parts yellow. 8

7a Nape and back yellow. Fig. 350.

529 EASTERN GOLDFINCH. *Spínus trístis trístis.*

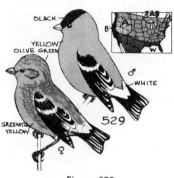

Figure 350

L. 5.1; W. 2.8. Bright canary yellow; black wings with single white wingbar; lesser wing-coverts yellow; black tail, marked with white. Upper tail coverts gray. ♀ Yellowish-brown above; dull yellowish below; wings and tail blackish. All birds are grayish-olive in winter with much reduced yellow markings.

529a PALE GOLDFINCH. *S. t. pállidus.* Larger; paler and grayer with more white on tail.

529b WILLOW GOLDFINCH. *S. t. salicámans.* Darker than 529 with wings and tail shorter.

Iowa, Minnesota, New Jersey and Washington have named the Goldfinch their state bird.

7b Upper part of head, nape and back blackish. Fig. 351.

530 ARKANSAS GOLDFINCH. *Spínus psáltria psáltria.*

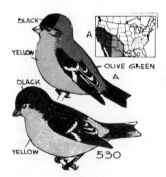

Figure 351

L. 4.5; W. 2.6. ♂ Crown glossy black; other upper parts and scapulars dark olive striped with black; wings black with large white patch at base of primaries and greater wing-coverts tipped with white; upper tail-coverts and tail black; under parts canary yellow. ♀ Dark olive-green not unlike ♀ of Northern Goldfinch.

530a GREEN-BACKED GOLDFINCH. *S. p. hesperóphilus.* Back of ♂ olive-green without black markings.

526.1 BRITISH GOLDFINCH. *Carduélis carduélis británnica.* Forehead crimson, back of head and neck, wings and tail black; under parts brown and white. Introduced from Europe into Eastern United States.

8a Chin and lower breast and belly white. Fig. 352.

604 DICKCISSEL. *Spíza americána.*

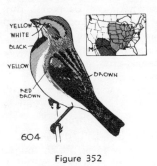

YELLOW
WHITE
BLACK
YELLOW
BROWN
RED
BROWN
604

Figure 352

L. 6; W. 3.2. ♂ Head gray, marked above and below eye and on forehead with yellow; back wings and tail dark brownish-gray; chin white, throat and breast with black patch above a long bright yellow area. (not unlike that of the Meadowlark); belly white. ♀ Somewhat lighter without the black patch on throat. The winter birds are less distinctly marked.

This is another bird that very definitely call its name. In the hottest hours of the day it may be seen sitting on post or telephone wire loudly chanting with, mechanical-like precision. *"Dick, dick, cissel, cissel, cissel."*

8b Chin and lower belly not white. 9

9a Chin and forehead black; wing-bars yellow. Fig. 353.

531 LAWRENCE'S GOLDFINCH. *Spínus láwrencei.*

BLACK
♂
YELLOW
BROWNISH GRAY
531
♀

Figure 353

L. 4.8; W. 2.7. ♂ Forehead and chin as pictured; black; upper parts brownish-gray sometimes tinged with olive-green, sides of head and body paler brownish-gray; throat and mid-breast yellow. ♀ Duller than ♂ with yellow less distinct.

Some folks know Goldfinches and also the Yellow Warbler only as "Wild Canaries". The Goldfinches have somewhat the advantage, in that their call is quite canary-like. A flock of these cheerful little fellows feeding in a field of dandelions make a picture long to be remembered.

9b Not as in 9a. 10

10a Stripe across forehead and over eyes, and belly yellow; bill thick, whitish; large white patch on wings. Fig. 354.

514 EASTERN EVENING GROSBEAK. ***Hesperiphóna vespertína vespertína.***

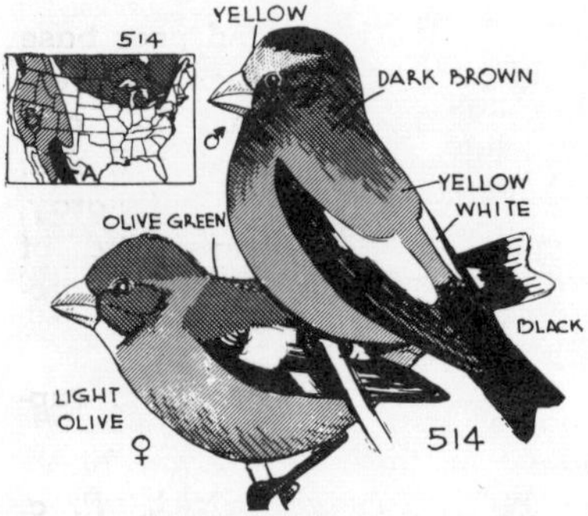

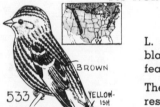

Figure 354

L. 8; W. 4.5. ♂ Crown black; olive-brown above, becoming dull yellow on rump, scapulars and belly yellow: wings black with very large white area; tail black. ♀ Brownish-gray tinged with yellow; wings and tail black.

514a MEXICAN EVENING GROSBEAK. *H. v. montána.* Yellow band narrower in front.

514b WESTERN EVENING GROSBEAK. *H. v. broóksi.* With longer and somewhat narrower bill.

10b Under parts dull white streaked with blackish; shows yellow in flight. Fig. 355.

533 NORTHERN PINE SISKIN. ***Spínus pínus pínus.***

Figure 355

L. 5; W. 2.8. Above grayish streaked with black; wings and tail fuscous; wings and tail feathers yellow at the base.

They belong to the pine forests, the song resembles that of the Goldfinch. Their yellow is conspicuous only in flight.

11a With a definite crest. 12

11b Without a pronounced crest. 13

12a Gray and red; bill very short, yellow. Fig. 356.

594 ARIZONA PYRRHULOXIA. ***Pyrrhulóxia sinuáta sinuáta.***

Figure 356

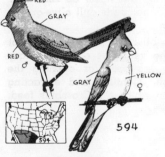

L. 8.8; W. 3.7. ♂ Above brownish-gray with less brown on head and neck. Markings of red on crest, wings, tail, throat and mid-breast; bill yellow in summer, horn-colored in winter. ♀ Lacking some ot the red markings of the male and more buffy especially below.

594a TEXAS PYRRHULOXIA. *P. s. texána.* Darker in color with larger and heavier bill. ♀ Grayer.

12b Entirely red (♂) or yellowish-brown with more or less red (♀). Bill heavy, red. Fig. 357.

    593 EASTERN CARDINAL. *Richmondéna cardinális cardinális.*

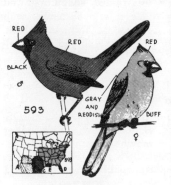

Figure 357

L. 8.3; W. 3.8. ♂ Throat and near base of bill black, otherwise rich rose-red. Bill red. ♀ Grayish around bill and throat; tail wings and crest dull red; other parts brownish or buffy-gray, lighter below. It is the state bird of Kentucky, Indiana, Illinois, North Carolina and Ohio.

593a ARIZONA CARDINAL. *R. c. supérba.* Larger and brighter red.

593c GRAY-TAILED CARDINAL. *R. c. canicaúda.* Wings a bit shorter; purer red and with smaller black area on throat.

593d FLORIDA CARDINAL. *R. c. floridána.* Smaller and darker.

593e LOUISIANA CARDINAL. *R. c. magniróstris.*

13a Bills crossed at tip. Figs. 358 and 359. 14

13b Bills normal, not crossed. 15

14a Rose pink; wings and tail black, the former with 2 prominent wing-bars. (♀ olive). Fig. 358.

    522 WHITEWINGED CROSSBILL. *Lóxia leucóptera.*

Figure 358

L. 6; W. 3.3. ♂ Body dull pink, rump brighter; belly light; wings and tail black, marked with white as shown in picture. ♀ Upper parts dull olive-green, grayer below.

The curious bills of these birds are not marks of the vengence of some angry god, but a provision for opening the scales of the Conifers and extracting the seeds on which the Crossbills feed.

155

14b Brick red, (♀ olive) wings and tail blackish; no wing-bars.
    Fig. 359.   521 RED CROSSBILL. *Lóxia curviróstra pusílla.*

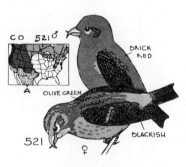

Figure 359

L. 6.2; W. 3.4. ♂ Brick red, brighter on rump, wings and tail fuscous. ♀ Dull olive-green, more yellow on rump; some whitish mixed with under parts.

521a MEXICAN CROSSBILL. *L. c. strícklandi.* Somewhat larger than 521.

521b NEWFOUNDLAND CROSSBILL. *L. c. pércna.* Winters in N. E. U. S.

521c SITKA CROSSBILL. *L. c. sitkénsis.*

521d BENDIRE'S CROSSBILL. *L. c. béndirei.* Noticeably larger than 521 and a lighter, brighter red.

15a Large rose-red spot on breast, otherwise black and white (♀ brown like a sparrow). Fig. 360.
    595 ROSE-BREASTED GROSBEAK. *Hedymeles ludoviciánus.*

Figure 360

L. 8.1; W. 4. ♂ Entire head and throat, back, tail and wings black, the latter marked with white; belly and rump white; breast rose. In winter with brown on upper parts and breast. ♀ Grayish-brown above marked with creamy-buff and whitish. The large bill helps to distinguish the ♀.

In the nesting season the male bird spends considerable time incubating the eggs and is so happy in his home duties that he sings as he sets. With his conspicious markings it's an especially careless thing to do. These birds eat quantities of Colorado potato beetles, which are spurned by most species.

15b Not as in 15a. 16

16a Under parts and rump red; back and wings green; head bluish-purple; ♀ dull green above, lighter below. Fig. 361.

601 PAINTED BUNTING. *Passerina ciris.*

Figure 361

L. 6; W. 2.8. ♂ Head and neck purplish-blue; back and parts of wings green; throat and other under parts vermilion red; rump and upper tail-coverts purplish-red. ♀ Plain dull green above, olive-yellowish beneath.

This and the following species, have, truly, the coat of many colors. They are beautifully decorated.

16b Not as in 16a. 17

17a Forehead and face blue; back of head red, back and under parts red-brown, wings and tail bluish. Fig. 362.

600 VARIED BUNTING. *Passerina versicolor versicolor.*

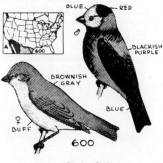

Figure 362

L. 5.5; W. 2.5. ♂ Marked and colored as in key; in winter duller colored. ♀ Grayish-brown above with olive tinge; tail and wings bluish; throat and belly dull whitish, other under parts grayish-brown, darkest on chest; deeper colored in winter.

600a BEAUTIFUL BUNTING. *P. v. pulchra.*

17b Not as in 17a. 18

18a Head marked at least in part with red. 20

18b Head not marked with red. 19

19a Breast brownish-black, (♂); slate-brownish, (♀); one white wing-
   bar. Fig. 363.   525 BLACK ROSY FINCH. *Leucosticte atrata.*

Figure 363

L. 6.7; W. 4.3. ♂ Forehead and part of
crown black; sides of crown and back
of head light ashy gray; under parts
brownish-black, much pink on feathers
of sides and rump; many of the wing
feathers edged with pink; bill black,
becoming yellowish in winter. ♀ Duller than ♂ with pink paler.

19b Breast light chestnut brown. Fig. 364.
        524 GRAY-CROWNED ROSY FINCH.
        Leucosticte tephrocotis tephrocotis.

Figure 364

L. 6.3; W. 4.2. Forehead and part of
crown black, back of head as pictured,
ash gray; neck, back scapulars and
breast chestnut-brown; wings, rump
and flanks with more or less pink; bill
black. ♀ Quite similar but paler and
duller.

524a HEPBURN'S ROSY FINCH. *L. t. littorális.* Similar to above but with more
gray on side of head (see picture).

524b SIERRA NEVADA ROSY FINCH.
L. t. dawsoni.

526 BLACK-CAPPED ROSY FINCH. *L.
austrális.* Similar to 524 but without any
evident gray on head.

20a Rump red or reddish; chin and throat red. .21

20b Rump whitish (sometimes with pink tinge); chin and upper throat blackish. Fig. 365.

528 COMMON REDPOLL. *Acánthis linária linária.*

Figure 365

L. 5.3. W. 2.8. ♂ Forward setting cap on head, bright red; back grayish-brown mixed with blackish; wings and tail darker with some white markings and 2 wing-bars; chin and upper throat blackish; breast pinkish, belly white; sides with fuscous streaks. ♀ Similar but more heavily striped below and lacking pink on breast and rump.

21a Back of head brownish. 22

21b Head wholly red (♂); olive-yellow in ♀ and young. Fig. 366.

515 CANADIAN PINE GROSBEAK. *Pinícola enucleátor leucúra.*

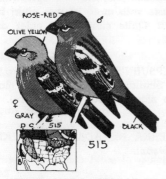

Figure 366

L. 9.1; W. 4.4. Head, breast and rump rather largely rose-red; back, wings and tail slate gray, the wings and tail darker; two very evident white wing-bars. ♀ Resembles the ♂ except that olive-yellow replaces the red.

515a ROCKY MOUNTAIN PINE GROS-BEAK. *P. e. montána.* Somewhat larger and darker.

515b CALIFORNIA PINE GROSBEAK. *P. e. califórnica.* With smaller bill and less red.

515c ALASKA PINE GROSBEAK. *P. e. alascénsis.* Larger but with paler colors.

515d KODIAK PINE GROSBEAK. *P. e. flámmula.* Still larger than 515c; brighter red and bill somewhat hooked.

22a Belly and part of breast streaked with brown; red streak over eye. Fig. 367.

519 COMMON HOUSE FINCH. *Carpódacus mexicánus frontális.*

Figure 367

L. 5.5; W. 3. Forehead, stripe over eye, rump and breast bright red. (sometimes dull to almost orange); under parts whitish striped with brown. ♀ A gray-brown striped sparrow-like bird; under parts whitish streaked with dusky.

Nests around houses like the English Sparrow.

519b SAN LUCAS HOUSE FINCH. *C. m. rubérrimus.* Smaller and somewhat less reddish than the above.

22b Belly and sides plain. Fig. 368.

517 EASTERN PURPLE FINCH. *Carpódacus purpúreus purpúreus.*

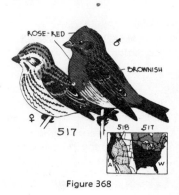

Figure 368

L. 6.2; W. 3.2. ♂ Striped sparrow-like bird strongly tinted on head, rump and breast with rose-red; belly usually white; wings and tail brownish. ♀ Brownish-gray sparrow-like bird with white stripe over eye and stripes on throat breast and belly. It is the state bird of New Hampshire.

517a CALIFORNIA PURPLE FINCH. *C. p. califórnicus.* Similar to above but with shorter wings.

518 CASSIN'S PURPLE FINCH. *C. cássini.* Very much like 517a but larger with somewhat paler breast and more definitely defined red spot on crown.

23a Sparrow like in appearance and size; back, usually the head and often the breast pattern of mixed brown or gray with white or black. 37

23b Not as in 23a; with rather large patches of solid colors, not with finely streaked grayish pattern. 24

24a Head black. 25

24b Head other than black. 29

25a Throat and upper breast black. 27

25b Throat and upper breast not black. 26

160

26a Throat, breast and under parts (except a collar on throat) whitish. Fig. 369.

      602 SHARPE'S SEEDEATER. *Sparóphila marolléti shárpei.*

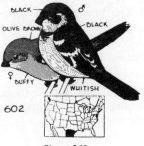

Figure 369

L. 4.4; W. 2.1. ♂ Top and sides of head, hind neck, back, scapulars, wings, tail and band across breast black; throat, breast (except for band), belly, spots as pictured on wing white; bill black. ♀ Olive-brown above, wings and tail dusky, the former with white markings; under parts lightly buffy. Young birds similar to ♀ but with buff wing-bars.

26b Throat and breast reddish-cinnamon or tawny. Fig. 370.

      596 BLACK-HEADED GROSBEAK. *Hedýmeles melanocéphalus melanocéphalus.*

Figure 370

L. 7.5; W. 4. ♂ Head, wings, upper tail coverts and tail black, the wings and tail marked with white as pictured; collar on hind neck, throat, breast, sides and rump tawny or buffy cinnamon; belly and under wing coverts lemon yellow. ♀ Grayish-brown to olive above, streaked with buff or whitish; face marked with white; under parts cinnamon-buffy.

596a ROCKY MOUNTAIN GROSBEAK. *H. m. pápago.*

27a Wings marked with white. 28

JUNCOS

27b No white on wings. Fig. 371.
  567a OREGON JUNCO. *Júnco oregánus oregánus.*

Figure 371

L. 6.2; W. 3. ♂ Head, neck and chest black, scapulars and back chestnut to reddish-sepia; Outer tail feathers wholly white; sides cinnamon; breast and ·belly white. ♀ Considerably lighter colored than ♂.

567b SHUFELDT'S JUNCO. *J. o. shúfeldti.* Less reddish on back.

567c THURBER'S JUNCO. *J. o. thúrberi.* Lighter colored on back and a bit larger;

567d POINT PINOS JUNCO. *J. o. pinósus.* Throat and chest slate instead of black.

567f MONTANA JUNCO. *J. o. montánus.* Head, neck and throat slate instead of black.

28a Wholly black except large white patch on wings and white edging of some wing and tail feathers. Fig. 372.
  605 LARK BUNTING. *Calamospiza melanócorys.*

Figure 372

L. 7; W. 3.5. ♂ Summer. Uniform black, sometimes with grayish sheen on back; wings and tail marked with white, as pictured. *Winter.* Grayish-brown streaked with dusky, under parts whitish; chin black. ♀ Grayish-brown and buffy with dark streaks; smaller white patch on wing; under parts white with streaks on breast and sides. Paler and more buffy in winter. Colorado claims it as its state bird.

28b Not as in 28a. 29

29a Back black, striped with white. Fig. 373.
588 ARCTIC TOWHEE. *Pípilo maculátus árcticus.*

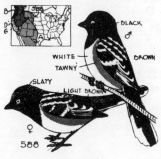

Figure 373

L. 8.8; W. 3.5. ♂ Head, neck and chest black (sometimes with a white spot on throat); back, wings and tail black or dark brown marked with white as pictured; breast and belly white; sides and flanks reddish-tawny. ♀ Similar but considerably lighter.

588a SPURRED TOWHEE. *P. m. montánus.* Shorter with larger white areas.

588b OREGON TOWHEE. *P. m. oregónus.* Smaller and darker.

588d SAN DIEGO TOWHEE. *P. m. megalónyx.* Larger and darker.

588f NEVADA TOWHEE. *P. m. curtátus.*

588g SACRAMENTO TOWHEE. *P. m. falcinéllus,*

29b Back plain black without white stripes. Fig. 374.
587 RED-EYED TOWHEE. *Pípilo erthroyphthálmus erthroyphthálmus.*

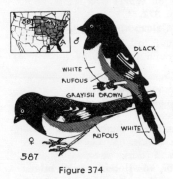

Figure 374

L. 8.4; W. 3.3. ♂ Head, throat, upper breast, upper parts, wings and tail black, the latter two marked with white as pictured; sides and flanks rufous; belly white; iris red. ♀ Grayish-brown above; sides rufous.

587a WHITE-EYED TOWHEE. *P. e. álleni.* Smaller with less white on wings and tail; iris white.

587b ALABAMA TOWHEE. *P. e. canáster.*

30a Head uniform slate gray (appearing almost black sometimes)...31

30b Not as in 30a. 34

31a Sides gray or slate colored. 32

31b Sides buffy-pink; back brownish drab. Fig. 375.
567g PINK-SIDED JUNCO. *Júnco medrnsi.*

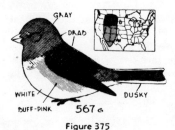

Figure 375

L. 6.6; W. 3.2. ♂ Head, neck and chest gray, lores blackish; back brownish-drab, sides and flanks pinkish; bill pinkish-white. ♀ Similar to ♂ but somewhat duller colored. Young birds obscurely streaked above.

32a Back gray or slate. 33

32b Back rufous. Fig. 376.
570b GRAY-HEADED JUNCO. *Júnco cániceps.*

Figure 376

L. 6.5; W. 3.4. Head, neck, breast, sides, rump and wing-coverts slate-gray; back between wings rufous, belly under tail-coverts and outer tail feathers white; bill pinkish; iris yellow.

570a RED-BACKED JUNCO. *J. phaeonótus dorsális.* Tail and bill longer; iris brown.

570b ARIZONA JUNCO. *J. p. palliátus.* Bill smaller, wings and tail shorter than 570; head and neck much lighter gray.

33a Wings marked with white as pictured. Fig. 377.
566 WHITE-WINGED JUNCO. *Júnco aikeni.*

Figure 377

L. 7; W. 3.6. ♂ Head, neck, breast, sides and upper parts slate-gray, darker on head; wings with two bars and other markings white; outer tail feathers white. ♀ Paler than ♂ and often with a brownish tinge.

33b Wings not marked with white. Fig. 378.
567 SLATE-COLORED JUNCO. *Júnco hyemális hyemális.*

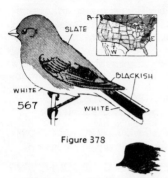

L. 6.3; W. 3.1. Grayish-slate with slight brownish tinge; belly and outer tail feathers white; mid-tail feathers blackish; bill flesh-color. ♀ Duller, a bit brownish; paler beneath.

567e CAROLINA JUNCO. *J. h. carolinénsis.* Slightly larger, not at all brownish; bill horn-color.

Figure 378

The plain gray, square cut "bib" and white tail feathers so conspicuous in flight are sure characters for these ever welcome visitors.

34a Above greenish or olive; under parts gray. 35

34b Unmarked bright brown above. 36

35a Crown rufous; throat white. Fig. 379.
592.1 GREEN-TAILED TOWHEE. *Oberholséria chlorúra.*

L. 7.4; W. 3.2. ♂ Upper parts olive-gray with tinges of yellow-green; crown and back of head rufous, streak on forehead and throat white; breast and sides gray; belly white; under tail-coverts light buff. ♀ Practically same as ♂ but sometimes a bit duller in color.

Figure 379

35b Top of head with two stripes of chestnut-brown separated by mid-stripe of olive-green; chestnut-brown streak through eye. Fig. 380.
586 TEXAS SPARROW. *Arremónops rufivirgátus rufivirgátus.*

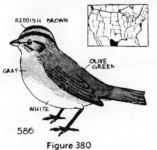

L. 6.4; W. 2.6. Plain grayish-olive-green above, striped on head as in key; under parts whitish-gray; white on belly; edge of wing bright yellow, bill and iris brown.

Figure 380

165

36a Throat and lower face pale pinkish-buff, flecked with dark brown or blackish. Fig. 381.

591 CANON TOWHEE. *Pípilo fúscus mesoleúcus.*

Figure 380

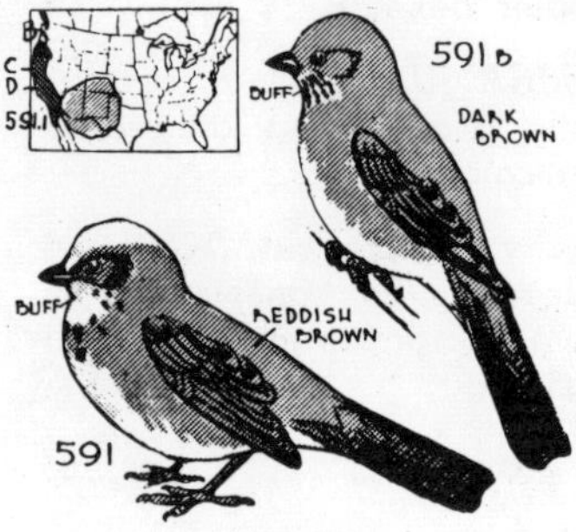

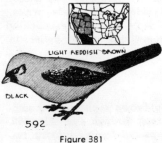

L. 9; W. 3.8. Upper parts rather uniform reddish-brown; mid-breast and belly whitish, sides brown; face, throat and upper breast light pinkish-buff with spots of brown or blackish; iris brown.

591b OREGON BROWN TOWHEE. *P. f. bullátus.* Larger and a bit darker.

591c SACRAMENTO BROWN TOWHEE. *P. f. cárolae.* Very dark brown.

591d SAN FRANCISCO BROWN TOWHEE. *P. f. pétulans.* Darker than 591.

591.1 CALIFORNIA TOWHEE. *P. f. crissális.* Larger and darker than 591.

591.1 ANTHONY'S TOWHEE. *P. f. senícula.* Smaller, darker and grayer than 591.

These last four species all belong to California.

36b Chin, throat and lores streaked with dusky or wholly so. Fig. 382.

592 ABERT'S TOWHEE. *Pípilo áberti.*

Figure 381

L. 9.7; W. 3.7. Light reddish-brown above, wings and tail somewhat darker; under parts paler brown; the lores and throat blackish; bill grayish-brown.

37a Breast or sides definitely striped. 59

37b No stripes on breast. (May be a few whisker marks on throat)... 38

38a Breast with single dark spot (or wholly black). 39

38b Not as in 38a. 43

39a Outer corners of tail white; cheek and head patches chestnut. Fig. 383.

WHITISH CHESTNUT

BLACK SPOT

552

Figure 383

552 EASTERN LARK SPARROW.
Chondéstes grammácus grammácus.

L. 6.3; W. 3.5. Sides of crown and ear-coverts chestnut; center of crown and line over eye whitish; line on throat and spot on breast black; upper parts brownish streaked with black; under parts white or whitish.

552a WESTERN LARK SPARROW. C. *g. strigátus.* Head markings and upper parts lighter; back browner with black stripes narrower.

39b Not as in 39a. **40**

40a Tail largely white; forehead and at least part of breast black...41

40b Not as in 40a. **42**

41a Entire underparts except throat black; nape chestnut. (♂); ♀ brownish sparrow-like but with much white on tail. Fig. 384.
538 .CHESTNUT-COLLARED LONGSPUR. *Calcárius ornátus.*

BLACK CHESTNUT
SPRING ♂

BROWN

♀

538

Figure 384

L. 6; W. 3.4. ♂ Summer. Top of head, stripe behind eye and entire under parts except throat black; back of neck rufous; stripe above eye, and throat white; cheeks buff. *Winter.* Black and rufous parts more or less brownish or buffy. ♀ Light grayish-buffy-brown with darker streaks; under parts light, sometimes with streaks.

41b Upper breast with large black spot as pictured. Fig. 385.
  539 MC COWN'S LONGSPUR. *Rhynchólophanes mccowni.*

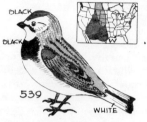

Figure 385

L. 6.1; W. 3.6. ♂ *Summer.* Head and breast marked with black as pictured; upper parts pale brownish-gray becoming brown on back; under parts whitish, tinged with pale gray at sides. *Winter.* Black concealed by brown or buff tips to feathers. ♀ Buffy-brown above, streaked with blackish; light beneath.

42a Crown rufous-red. No whisker marks. Fig. 386.
  559 EASTERN TREE SPARROW. *Spizélla arbórea arbórea.*

Figure 386

L. 6.4; W. 3. Under parts light with black spot at center of breast rather indistinct; line over eye grayish; line back of eye rufous; back streaked buff, brown and black; rump pale.

559a WESTERN TREE SPARROW. *S. a. ochrácea.* Paler in color with somewhat longer wings and tail; black streaks on back more narrow.

42b Crown gray; forehead white; whisker marks on throat. Fig. 387.
  574 BELL'S SPARROW. *Amphispíza bélli bélli.*

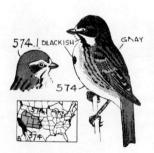

Figure 387

L. 6; W. 2.7. Brownish-slate-gray above becoming browner on back, sometimes with narrow blackish streaks; wings and tail blackish; head marked with white as pictured; breast with black or grayish spot; buff or pale yellowish on flanks and edge of wings.

574.1 NORTHERN SAGE SPARROW. *A. nevadénsis nevadénsis.* Paler, grayer and definitely larger than 574; whisker marks much narrower.

574.1b CALIFORIA SAGE SPARROW. *A. n. canéscens.*

43a Principally white, with markings as pictured of rust-brown. Fig. 388.

      534 EASTERN SNOW BUNTING. *Plectróphenax nivális nivális.*

L. 6.9; W. 4.1. ♂ *Summer.* Head, neck, rump and under parts white; back, scapulars and outer primaries black. *Winter.* Black parts become rusty-brown sometimes streaked with blackish. ♀ Similar to male, but with more black or brown than ♂.

This is very definitely a bird of winter snows, so it is not seen at all in most of our territory during summer. It is a weed seed feeder.

Figure 388

43b Not as in 43a. **44**

44a Throat or chin black. **45**

44b Throat and chin not black. **48**

45a Only chin and lores black. Fig. 389.

      565 MEXICAN BLACK-CHINNED SPARROW.
        Spizélla atrogulàris atrogulàris.

L. 5.7; W. 2.4. Head and neck gray, with lores, chin and sometimes part of throat black; back reddish-brown streaked with black; tail and wings darker; belly white. The female closely resembles the male but may have the chin markings duller.

565a CALIFORNIA BLACK-CHINNED SPAR-ROW. *S. a. cána.* Smaller, and with the lores less decidedly black.

Figure 389

45b Chin and breast black. **46**

46a Face black in spring; belly yellowish in winter; walks, does not hop. Fig. 390.

  536 LAPLAND LONGSPUR. *Calcárius lappónicus lappónicus.*

Figure 390

L. 6; W. 3.8. ♂ *Spring.* Face, throat and upper breast as pictured black, with stripe of white or buff; sides with broad black stripe; rest of under parts white. *Winter.* Black only on crown, with obscure grayish spot on throat and breast, belly yellowish. ♀ Similar in markings to winter ♂, size smaller.

536a ALASKA LONGSPUR. *C. l. alascénsis.* Winter plumage lighter than 536.

These two birds enter our territory only in the winter months.

46b Not as in 46a. **47**

47a Crown gray, margined in front and on sides with black; face with two white lines. Fig. 391.

  573 BLACK-THROATED SPARROW. *Amphispíza bilineáta bilineáta.*

Figure 391

L. 5.4; W. 2.5. Gray above becoming brownish on back; tail blackish with margin of white for part or entire length; lores, chin, throat and breast as pictured, black; rest of under parts white.

573a DESERT SPARROW. *A. b. desertícola.* A bit larger than 573, paler and browner above.

47b Crown, throat and breast black. Fig. 392.

  553 HARRIS'S SPARROW. *Zonotríchia quérula.*

Figure 392

L. 7.5; W. 3.5. Crown, lores, throat and breast black; cheeks buffy-gray; nape and back gray, the latter striped with black; rump brownish; tail gray; belly white; bill pinkish.

170

48a Crown black and white. 49

48b Crown not black and white. 50

49a Throat white; yellow on bend of wing and in front of eye.
Fig. 393. 558 WHITE-THROATED SPARROW. *Zonotríchia albicóllis.*

558

Figure 393

L. 6.7; W. 2.9. Crown black with white stripe through its middle and one on either side; back rufous, marked with black and with white, tail brownish gray; under parts grayish; throat with conspicuous white patch; spot in front of eye and bend on wing yellow.

This well-tailored, friendly bird is a favorite among bird lovers.

49b Throat gray like neck and breast; no yellow markings. Fig. 394.
554 WHITE-CROWNED SPARROW.
Zonotríchia leucóphrys leucóphrys.

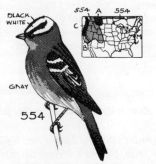

554

Figure 394

L. 6.9; W. 3. Crown white and black as pictured; neck and breast plain gray; back gray with dark brown stripes; tail blackish; belly white; flanks and under tail-coverts pale buff.

554a GAMBEL'S SPARROW. *Z. l. gámbeli.* Lores whitish; bill yellowish.

554b NUTTALL'S SPARROW. *Z. l. núttalli.* Darker in color and smaller than 554a.

554c PUGET SOUND SPARROW. *Z. l. pugeténsis.*

The areas marked on the map are the breeding ranges. These birds may be seen throughout much of the U. S. when migrating.

50a Crown rufous-red. 51

50b Crown not rufous-red. 54

51a Black line through eye; white line over it. Fig. 395.
    560 EASTERN CHIPPING SPARROW. *Spizélla passerína passerína.*

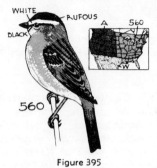

L. 5.4; W. 2.7. Forehead, bill and line back of eye black; throat and line over eye grayish-white; back brownish streaked with black; rump slate gray. The rufous crown becomes streaked in the fall.

560a WESTERN CHIPPING SPARROW. S. *p. arizónae.* Somewhat larger and paler. These friendly little birds delight to live and rear their young around our houses and gardens. It is easy to win their confidence.

Figure 395

51b Not as in 51a. 52

52a Throat gray. 53
52b Throat white. Fig. 396.
    584 SWAMP SPARROW. *Melospíza georgiána.*

L. 5.9; W. 2.3. Forehead and line back of eye blackish; grayish line over eye; back with broad blackish streaks; tail reddish-brown, rounded at tip; breast gray; throat and mid-belly white. In winter the crown is streaked with black and the breast is tinged with brown.

Figure 396

53a With black whisker marks on throat. Fig. 397.
    580 RUFOUS-CROWNED SPARROW. *Aimóphila rúficeps rúficeps.*

L. 6; W. 2.4. Crown chestnut, darker on forehead, sometimes with obscure stripe at middle; back grayish-brown with broad chestnut stripes; tail light brown; under parts pale buffy-brown.

580a SCOTT'S SPARROW. A. r. *scótti.* Larger with broader streaks on back.

580b ROCK SPARROW. A. r. *eremoeca.* Larger and paler and grayer than 580.

580d ASHY SPARROW. A. r. *canéscens.*

Figure 397

53b Throat unmarked; bill pink to reddish-brown. Fig. 398.
563 EASTERN FIELD SPARROW. *Spizélla pusílla pusílla.*

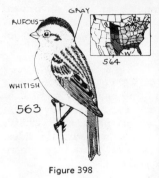

L. 5.7; W. 2.5. Crown rufous; gray line over eye; back rufous finely striped with black and ashy; wing-bars prominent. Duller in winter. Its winter range often overlaps much of its breeding area.

563a WESTERN FIELD SPARROW. *S. p. arenácea.* Wings and tail much longer; grayer in color.

564 WORTHEN'S SPARROW. *S. wórtheni.* Similar to 563a but with shorter tail, wing-bars less distinct and side of head gray.

Figure 398

54a Crown more or less yellow, bordered with black. Fig. 399.
557 GOLDEN-CROWNED SPARROW. *Zonotríchia coronáta.*

L. 6.4; W. 3.2. Top of head black with broad mid-stripe of olive-yellow; upper parts grayish olive-brown; the back and scapulars striped with black; under parts brownish-gray, paler on throat and chin; belly whitish. Female often paler than male.

Figure 399

54b Not as in 54a. 55

55a Crown and back with stripes. 56

55b Crown plain, not striped. 57

56a Crown brown with fine stripes of black. Fig. 400.
562 BREWER'S SPARROW. *Spizélla bréweri bréweri.*

L. 5.5; W. 2.5. Back pale brown with rather wide black stripes; rump and upper tail-coverts with stripes somewhat indistinct; tail grayish-brown; under parts dull whitish, breast and sides with buffy-gray shading.

562a TIMBERLINE SPARROW. *S. b. tavérneri.* It breeds north of our mapped area but migrates into our Rocky Mountain regions.

Figure 400

56b Crown striped with light gray. 57

57a Middle of crown with light stripe; ear-patch as pictured, brown; slender whisker marks on throat. Fig. 401.

561 CLAY-COLORED SPARROW. Spizélla pállida.

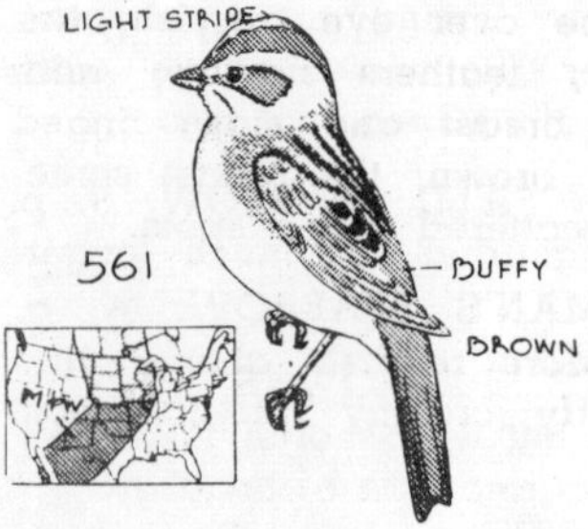

LIGHT STRIPE

561

DUFFY

BROWN

L. 5.6; W. 2.4. Crown light brown with black striping and center stripe of light gray; back and scapulars buffy-brown, tail darker; under parts dull whitish with tinges of buff on breast and sides. In winter with less black and more buffy in the plumage.

Figure 401

57b Crown streaked with light gray; unmarked below. Fig. 402.

546 EASTERN GRASSHOPPER SPARROW. Ammódramus savannárum austrális.

REDDISH
BROWN
BLACK
AND
GRAY

546

L. 5.4; W. 2.4. Upper parts mixed reddish-brown, ashy, buff and black; bend of wing yellow; orange mark over eye; tail dark, its individual feathers pointed; breast and sides buffy, belly white.

546a WESTERN GRASSHOPPER SPARROW. A. s. bimaculátus. More rusty-brown above; wings and tail longer.

546b FLORIDA GRASSHOPPER SPARROW. A. s. floridánus. Smaller than 546; darker above and paler below.

Figure 402

58a Light brown above, streaked with light gray. Fig. 403.

578 CASSIN'S SPARROW. Aimóphila cássini.

LIGHT
BROWN

L. 6.2; W. 2.6. Head with obscure blackish streaks; wing feathers margined with grayish; tail brownish-gray; breast, sides, and belly dull white, often with dusky tinges.

576 BOTTERI'S SPARROW. A. bótterii bótterii. Similar but duller colored and still less evidence of stripes on crown; under parts paler. Its range is much the same as that of 578.

578

Figure 403

53b Gray above with broad streaks of chestnut-brown. Fig. 404.
575 PINE-WOODS SPARROW. *Aimóphila aestivális aestivális.*

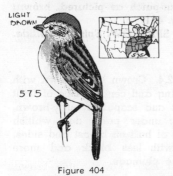

L. 5.8; W. 2.5. Gray above with broad streaks of chestnut and finer streaks of black; line over eye grayish; tail blackish-gray, feathers narrow; mid-belly white; breast and sides tinged with grayish brown; the breast sometimes with scattered black spots.

575a BACHMAN'S SPARROW. *A. a. báchmani.* More reddish above; line over eye buffy; creamy buff on breast and sides.

Figure 404

59a Outer tail feathers white. 60

59b Outer tail feathers not white. 63

60a Hind toenail very long, wing-coverts not rufous. 61

60b Hind toenail shorter, wing-coverts bright rufous. Fig. 405.
540 EASTERN VESPER SPARROW. *Pooécetes gramíneus gramíneus.*

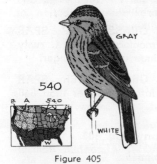

L. 6.1; W. 3. Brownish-gray above with streaks of black and buffy; wings and tail darker; lesses coverts bright rufous; white of outer tail feathers shows very plainly in flight; beneath white with streaks of black and buff.

540a WESTERN VESPER SPARROW. *P. g. confínis.* Larger and somewhat paler.

540b OREGON VESPER SPARROW. *P. g. affínis.* Smaller than 540; browner above, buffy below.

Figure 405

61a Under parts yellowish or buffy. Fig. 406.
537 SMITH'S LONGSPUR. *Calcárius píctus.*

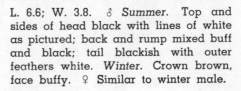

L. 6.6; W. 3.8. ♂ Summer. Top and sides of head black with lines of white as pictured; back and rump mixed buff and black; tail blackish with outer feathers white. *Winter.* Crown brown, face buffy. ♀ Similar to winter male.

175

Figure 406

61b Not as in 61a. 62

62a Only small middle part of tail dark, remainder white. CHESTNUT-COLORED LONGSPUR. See Fig. 384.

62b Tail mostly dark, white outer margins narrow. LAPLAND LONGSPUR. See Fig. 390.

63a Large spot at center of breast. Fig. 407.
    581 EASTERN SONG SPARROW. *Melospiza melódia melódia.*

Figure 407

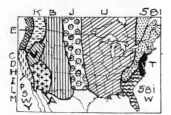

L. 6.3; W. 2.5. Crown rufous-brown parted with a gray line and another over the eye; back rufous-brown streaked and margined with black and grayish; mid-belly white; under markings brown and black.

The Song Sparrow is widely distributed and represents the extreme in the naming of subspecies. We are not attempting to give the distinguishing characters, but list the subspecies and show the approximate distribution of those living within our area.

581a DESERT SONG SPARROW. *M. m. sáltonis.*
581b MOUNTAIN SONG SPARROW. *M. m. fállax.*
581c HEERMANN'S SONG SPARROW. *M. m. heermanni.*
581d SAMUEL'S SONG SPARROW. *M. m. samuélis.*
581e RUSTY SONG SPARROW. *M. m. mórphna.*
581f SOOTY SONG SPARROW. *M. m. rufina.*
581g BROWN'S SONG SPARROW. *M. m. rivuláris.*
581h SANTA BARBARA SONG SPARROW. *M. m. gramínea.*
581i SAN CLEMENTE SONG SPARROW. *M. m. cleméntae.*
581j DAKOTA SONG SPARROW. *M. m. júddi.*
581k MERRILL'S SONG SPARROW. *M. m. mérilli.*
581l ALAMEDA SONG SPARROW. *M. m. pusillula.*
581m SAN DIEGO SONG SPARROW. *M. m. coóperi.*
581n YAKUTAT SONG SPARROW. *M. m. caurína.*

581o KENAI SONG SPARROW. *M. m. kenaieńsis.*
581p MENDOCINO SONG SPARROW. *M. m. cleoneńsis.*
581q BISCHOFF'S SONG SPARROW. *M. m. insiǵnis.*
581r ALEUTIAN SONG SPARROW. *M. m. sanáka.*
581s SUISUN SONG SPARROW. *M. m. maxilláris.*
581t ATLANTIC SONG SPARROW. *M. m. atlántica.*
581u MISSISSIPPI SONG SPARROW. *M. m. beáta.*
581v MODOC SONG SPARROW. *M. m. fisherélla.*
581w SAN MIGUEL SONG SPARROW. *M. m. microńyx.*
581x CORONADOS SONG SPARROW. *M. m. ҫoronatórum.*
581y MODESTO SONG SPARROW. *M. m. maílliardi.*

63b Without a definite large spot on breast. 64

64a Large for a sparrow; breast heavily marked; tail reddish. Fig. 408.
585 EASTERN FOX SPARROW. *Passerella iliaca iliaca.*

585

Figure 408

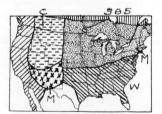

L. 7.3; W. 3.4. Rufous-brown above without any black markings; tail and upper tail-coverts bright rufous; under parts marked with rufous; mid-belly white.

As with the Song Sparrow we are only listing the subspecies. There is much overlapping of their ranges especially during their migration. The map shows the approximate breeding, migratory and winter range of the Eastern and the Slate-colored Fox Sparrows. The others are known in the Pacific States where they either breed or winter.

585a SHUMAGIN FOX SPARROW. *P. i. unalaschcénsis.*
585b THICK-BILLED FOX SPARROW. *P. i. megarhýncha.*
585c SLATE-COLORED FOX SPARROW. *P. i. schistácea.*
585d STEPHEN'S FOX SPARROW. *P. i. stephénsi.*
585e SOOTY FOX SPARROW. *P. i. fulginósa.*
585f KODIAK FOX SPARROW. *P. i. insuláris.*
585g TOWNSEND'S FOX SPARROW. *P. i. tównsendi.*
585h ALBERTA FOX SPARROW. *P. i. altivágans.*
585i WARNER MOUNTAINS FOX SPARROW. *P. i. fúlva.*

585j TRINITY FOX SPARROW. *P. i. brevicaúda.*

585k VALDEZ FOX SPARROW. *P. i. sinuósa.*

585l YAKUTAT FOX SPARROW. *P. i. annéctens.*

585m INYO FOX SPARROW. *P. i. canéscens.*

585n MONO FOX SPARROW. *P. i. monoénsis.*

585o YOSEMITE FOX SPARROW. *P. i. maripósae.*

64b Not as in 64a. **65**

65a Ground color of upper breast dark. **66**

65b Ground color of upper breast not dark. **67**

66a Yellow spot at upper front of eye, upper breast gray. Fig. 409.
550 NORTHERN SEASIDE SPARROW.
Ammospiza maritima maritima.

Figure 409

L. 6; W. 2.5. Yellow on bend of wing and at front of eye; gray-olive-green above, breast buffy tinged in winter and with gray streaks; mid-belly and throat white. Found in salt marshes. This and the eight others listed below are scattered along the Atlantic and Gulf coasts as shown on the map. Their breeding and wintering ranges are mixed and overlapping.

550a **SCOTT'S SEASIDE SPARROW.** *A. m. peninsulae.* Darker but somewhat olive above.

550b **TEXAS SEASIDE SPARROW.** *A. m. sennetti.* Smaller, paler and more buffy.

550c **LOUISIANA SEASIDE SPARROW.** *A. m. fisheri.* Very dark above, buffy below.

550d **MACGILLIVRAY'S SEASIDE SPARROW.** *A. m. macgillivraii.* Darker; back broadly streaked with black.

550e **WAKULLA SEASIDE SPARROW.** *A. m. juncicola.*

550f **HOWELL'S SEASIDE SPARROW.** *A. m. howelli.*

551 **DUSKY SEASIDE SPARROW.** *A. nigrescens.* Black above, streaked with olive and gray.

551.1 **CAPE SABLE SEASIDE SPARROW.** *A. mirábilis.*

66b Without yellow spot; upper breast with band of buffy. Fig. 410.
583 LINCOLN'S SPARROW. *Melospiza lincolni lincolni.*

L. 5.8; W. 2.5. Brownish above streaked with black and gray; below white with a broad buff band on breast and at sides of throat; sides buffy.

583a FORBUSH'S SPARROW. *M. l. gracilis.* A highly similar subspecies breeds in Alaska but winters in California (lucky fellow!).

Figure 410

67a Breast stripes short. **68**

67b Breast stripes longer. **69**

68a Crown striped with ochre and black. Fig. 411.
545 BAIRD'S SPARROW. *Ammodramus bairdi.*

L. 5.6; W. 2.8. Head buffy or ochre, lighter on sides and practically white on chin and throat; crown with black streaks; upper parts light brown; white to pale buff below; iris brown.

By now the reader has discovered that our country is filled with native sparrows of many species and subspecies. They are a friendly lot of little fellows though some are very shy. If time hangs heavily on your hands we would suggest that you get out into the open and learn to recognize as many of them as you can. You will likely die at old age, young of heart, but with a few sparrows of which you are yet none too certain.

If this task should prove too short, the Warblers with all their seasonal variations could occupy some time.

Figure 411

68b Center stripe on crown ashy-blue, margined with black and brown. Fig. 412.

549 SHARP-TAILED SPARROW. *Ammospiza caudacúta caudacúta.*

Figure 412

L. 5.9; W. 2.3. Brownish olive-green above; crown olive-brown with blue-gray line at middle; face marked with gray and buff; under parts whitish, tinged with buff on breast and sides.

549.1 NELSON'S SPARROW. *A. c. nélsoni.* Smaller and darker above; the throat buff.

549.1 ACADIAN SPARROW. *P. n. subvirgáta.* Paler than 549 with breast, throat and sides tinged with buff and faintly striped with gray.

69a Tail definitely notched; mid-line of crown buffy. Fig. 413.

542a EASTERN SAVANNAH SPARROW. *Passérculus sandwichénsis savánna.*

Figure 413

L. 5.7; W. 2.6. Brownish-black above striped with buffy and rufous; pale yellow on bend of wing and in front of eye; tail blackish; white below with streaks of black and rufous.

542 ALEUTIAN SAVANNAH SPARROW. *P. s. sandwichénsis.* Larger but not so brown as above.

541 IPSWICH SPARROW. *P. prínceps.* Similar but much paler than EASTERN SAVANNAH SPARROW.

542b WESTERN SAVANNAH SPARROW. *P. s. alaudínus.* Paler than EASTERN SAVANNAH SPARROW.

542c BRYANT'S SPARROW. *P. s. bryánti.* Smaller and darker than 542a.

542d LABRADOR SAVANNAH SPARROW. *P. s. labrodórius.* Darker with more streaks on breast.

542e NEVADA SAVANNAH SPARROW. *P. s. nevadénsis.*

543 BELDING'S SPARROW. *P. béldingi.* Very dark; heavily streaked with black above. Salt marshes of S. Calif.

544 LARGE-BILLED SPARROW. *P. rostrátus rostrátus.* Light brown above tinged with gray; bill thick. Southern and Lower Calif.

544a SAN LUCUS SPARROW. *P. r. guttátus.* Darker but with smaller and slimmer bill than 544. Lower Calif.

69b Tail not notched; outer tail feathers shorter than middle ones...70

70a Nape olive-green with fine streaks of black. Fig. 414.
     547 EASTERN HENSLOW'S SPARROW.
     Passerhérbulus hénslowi súsurrans.

L. 5; W. 2.2. Back rufous-brown; top and sides of head and nape pale olive-green; bend of wing pale yellow; white beneath, streaked with black.

547a WESTERN HENSLOW'S SPARROW. *P. h. hénslowi.* Paler than 547.

Figure 414

70b Nape rufous; throat and mid-breast plain. Fig. 415.
   548 LECONTE'S SPARROW. *Passerhérbulus caudacútus.*

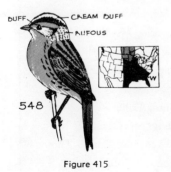

L. 5; W. 2. Back blackish with markings of rufous; nape rufous brown; line over eye buff; belly white, breast and sides with tinge of buff; usually only the sides streaked with black.

Figure 415

OUR NATIONAL AND STATE BIRDS

Man likes to select symbols. Just as the Bald Eagle has long been the official bird for emblems of the United States, each state has selected its state bird by action of its legislature or sometimes otherwise. The full list follows:

Alabama; Flicker	Montana; Western Meadowlark
Arizona; Cactus Wren	Nebraska; Western Meadowlark
Arkansas; Mockingbird	Nevada; Mountain Bluebird
California; California Quail	New Hampshire; Purple Finch
Colorado; Lark Bunting	New Jersey; Goldfinch
Connecticut; Robin	New Mexico; Road-runner
Delaware; Blue Hen Chicken	New York; Eastern Bluebird
District of Columbia; Wood Thrush	North Carolina; Cardinal
	North Dakota; Western Meadowlark
Florida; Mockingbird	Ohio; Cardinal
Georgia; Brown Thrasher	Oklahoma; Bob-white
Idaho; Mountain Bluebird	Oregon; Western Meadowlark
Illinois; Cardinal	Pennsylvania; Ruffed Grouse
Indiana; Cardinal	Rhode Island; Bob-white
Iowa; Goldfinch	South Carolina; Mockingbird
Kansas; Western Meadowlark	South Dakota; Ring-necked Pheasant
Kentucky; Cardinal	
Louisiana; Brown Pelican	Tennessee; Mockingbird
Maine;Black-capped Chickadee	Texas; Mockingbird
Maryland; Baltimore Oriole	Utah; California Gull
Massachusetts; Black-capped Chickadee	Vermont; Hermit Thrush
	Virginia; Robin
Michigan; Robin	Washington; Goldfinch
Minnesota; Goldfinch	West Virginia; Tufted Titmouse
Mississippi; Mockingbird	Wisconsin; Robin
Missouri; Eastern Bluebird	Wyoming; Western Meadowlark

INDEX AND PICTURED GLOSSARY

It will be noted that the uncapitalized items represent the species or subspecies names of the birds described in this book, and that in each case they appear under the genus name with which they are associated in the scientific name.

Figure 418

Figure 419

Figure 420

Figure 421

INDEX

texanus, 24
umbrinus, 23

C

Cabanis's Woodpecker, 68
Cactus Woodpecker, 67
Cactus Wren, 104
Cairn's Warbler, 139
Calamospiza, 162
  melanocorys, 162
Calaveras Warbler, 135
Calcarius, 167
  alascensis, 170
  lapponicus, 170
  ornatus, 167
  pictus, 175
California Black-chinned
  Sparrow, 169
California Blue Gros-
  beak, 151
California Bush-Tit, 98
California Condor, 17
California Cowbird, 143
California Creeper, 72
California Cuckoo, 40
California Horned Lark, 71
California Jay, 95
California Pine Gros-
  beak, 159
California Purple Finch, 160
California Pygmy Owl, 46
California Quail, 35
California Sage Sparrow, 168
California Screech Owl, 42
California Shrike, 117
California Spotted Owl, 48
California Thrasher, 106
California Towhee, 166
California Woodpecker, 66
California Yellow Warb-
  ler, 128
Calling birds, 8
Callipepla, 34
  castanogastris, 34
  pollida, 34
  squamata, 34
Callichelidon, 89
  cyaneoviridis, 89
Calliope Hummingbird, 54
Calothorax, 57
  lucifer, 57
Calypte, 57
  anna, 54
  costae, 57
Camera, 9
Campephilus, 60
  principalis, 60
Camptostoma, 83
  imberbe, 83
Conachites, 31
  canace, 31
  canadensis, 31
  franklini, 31
Canada Jay, 93
Canada Spruce Grouse, 31
Canada Warbler, 137
Canadian Pine Grosbeak, 159
Canon Towhee, 166
Canon Wren, 102
Cape May Warbler, 126
Cape Sable Seaside Spar-
  row, 178
Caprimulgiformes, 49
Cardellina, 124
  rubrifrons, 124
Cardinal, 155

Carduelis, 152
  britannica, 152
  carduelis, 152
Carnivorous: feeding on
  other animals.
Carolina Chickadee, 100
Carolina Junco, 165
Carolina Paroquet, 14
Carolina Wren, 105
Carpodacus, 160
  californicus, 160
  cassini, 160
  frontalis, 160
  mexicanus, 160
  purpureus, 160
  ruberrimus, 160
Cassidix, 141
  major, 141
  mexicanus, 141
Cassin's Kingbird, 82
Cassin's Purple Finch, 160
Cassin's Sparrow, 174
Cassin's Vireo, 120
Catbird, 107
Cathartes, 18
  aura, 18
  septentrionalis, 18
Catherpes, 102
  conspersus, 102
  mexicanus, 102
  punctulatus, 102
Caudal: relating to the tail.
Cedar Waxwing, 116
Centrocercus, 31
  urophasianus, 31
Centurus, 64
  aurifrons, 64
  carolinus, 66
  uropygialis, 64
Ceophloeus, 60
  abieticola, 60
  floridanus, 60
  picinus, 60
  pileatus, 60
Cere: soft swollen area at
  base of upper bill. Fig.
  422.

Figure 422

Certhia, 72
  albescens, 72
  americana, 72
  familiaris, 72
  montana, 72
  occidentalis, 72
  zelotes, 72
Certhiidae, 72
Cerulean Warbler, 139
Chachalaca, 29
Chaetura, 52
  pelagica, 52
  vauxi, 52
Chamaea, 75
  fasciata, 75
  henshawi, 75
  phaea, 75
  rufula, 75
Chamaeidae, 75
Chamaethlypis, 134
  poliocephala, 134

Check numbers, 6
Cherrie's Nighthawk, 51
Chestnut-backed Blue-
  bird, 110
Chestnut-backed Chicka-
  dee, 98
Chestnut-bellied Scaled
  Quail, 34
Chestnut-collared Long-
  spur, 167
Chestnut-sided Warbler, 129
Chickadee, 98, 100
Chicken, 32
Chihuahua Woodpecker, 68
Chimney Swift, 52
Chin: At base of lower bill.
  Fig. 423.

Figure 423

Chinese Spotted Dove, 37
Chipping Sparrow, 172
Chloroceryle, 59
  americana, 59
  septentrionalis, 59
Chondestes, 167
  grammacus, 167
  strigatus, 167
Chordeiles, 51
  acutipennis, 51
  aserriensis, 51
  chapmani, 51
  henryi, 51
  hesperis, 51
  howelli, 51
  minor, 51
  sennetti, 51
  texensis, 51
Chuck-will's-widow, 49
Cinclus, 76
  mexicanus, 76
  unicolor, 76
Circus, 20
  hudsonius, 20
Cistothorus, 103
  stellaris, 103
Clarke's Nutcracker, 90
Classes, 5
Clay-colored Sparrow, 174
Cliff Swallow, 87
Clutch, 7
Coahuila Cliff Swallow, 87
Coast Bush-Tit, 98
Coast Jay, 94
Coast Pygmy Owl, 46
Coast Wren-Tit, 75
Coccyzus, 40
  americanus, 40
  erythropthalmus, 40
  maynardi, 40
  minor, 40
  occidentalis, 40
Colaptes, 62, 63
  auratus, 62
  cafer, 63
  chrysoides, 63
  collaris, 63
  luteus, 62
  mearnsi, 63

INDEX

Colinus, 33
  floridanus, 33
  ridgwayi, 33
  texanus, 33
  virginianus, 33
Collar: ring of different colored feathers encircling
  the neck. Fig. 424.

Figure 424

Columba, 36, 38
  fasciata, 38
  flavirostris, 38
  livia, 36
Columbia Chickadee, 98
Columbia Sharp-tailed
  Grouse, 32
Columbiformes, 36
Columbigallina, 38
  pallescens, 38
  passerina, 38
Common House Finch, 160
Common name, 5
Common Redpoll, 159
Common Rock Wren, 105
Compsothlypidae, 122
Compsothlypis, 136
  americana, 136
  nigrilora, 136
  pitiayumi, 136
  pusilla, 136
Condor, 17
Connecticut Warbler, 136
Contour feather, 3
Conuropsis, 14
  carolinensis, 14
Cooper's Hawk, 25
Cooper's Tanager, 149
Coppery-tailed Trogon, 16
Coraciiformes, 59
Coragyps, 18
  atratus, 18
Coronado's Song Spar-
  row, 177
Corthylio, 114
  calendula, 114
  cineraceus, 114
  grinnelli, 114
Corvidae, 90, 95
Corvus, 91, 92
  · brachyrhynchos, 91
  caurinus, 91
  corax, 91
  cryptoleucus, 91
  hesperis, 91
  ossifragus, 92
  pascuus, 91
  paulus, 91
  principalis, 91
  sinuatus, 91
Costa's Hummingbird, 57
Couch's Jay, 94
Couch's Kingbird, 81
Coues's Flycatcher, 84
Coverts: feathers covering a
  part.

Cowbird, 143
Creepers, 72
Crest: tuft of feathers on
  top of head. Fig. 425.

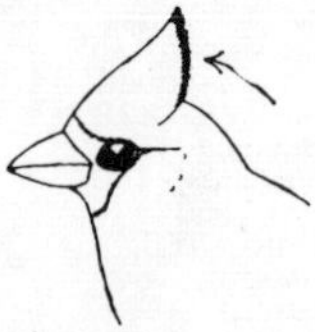

Figure 425

Crested Flycatcher, 82
Crested Mynah, 76
Crissal Thrasher, 107
Crossbill, 155, 156
Crotophaga, 39
  ani, 39
  sulcirostris, 39
Crown: region on·top of
  head. Fig. 426.

Figure 426

Crows, 90-92
Cryptoglaux, 46, 47
  acadica, 47
  funerea, 46
  richardsoni, 46
Cuckoo-like Birds, 39
Cuckoos, 40
Cuculiformes, 39
Curved: referring to bills or
  other parts. Fig. 427.

Figure 427

Curve-billed Thrasher, 106
Cyanocephalus, 90
Cyanocitta, 93
  annectens, 94
  carbonacea, 94
  cristata, 93
  diademata, 94
  florincola, 93
  frontalis, 94
  semplei, 93
  stelleri, 94
Cynanthus, 56
  latirostris, 56
Cyrtonyx, 34
  mearnsi, 34
  montezumae, 34

D

Dakota Song Sparrow, 176

Dendragapus, 32
  fulginosus, 32
  obscurus, 32
  richardsoni, 32
Dendrocia, 122, 125-129,
  132, 133, 137, 139
  aestiva, 128
  albilora, 137
  auduboni, 129
  brewsteri, 128
  caerulescens, 139
  cairnsi, 139
  castanea, 125
  cerulea, 139
  chrysoparia, 132
  collinsi, 133
  coronata, 129
  discolor, 133
  dominica, 137
  florida, 133
  fusca, 125
  graciae, 133
  hypochrysea, 126
  kirtlandi, 138
  magnolia, 137
  nigrifrons, 129
  occidentalis, 127
  palmarum, 126
  pensylvanica, 129
  pinus, 133
  sonorana, 128
  striata, 122
  tigrina, 126
  townsendi, 132
  virens, 132
  waynei, 132
Derby Flycatcher, 81
Desert Horned Lark, 71
Desert Poor-will, 50
Desert Song Sparrow, 176
Desert Sparrow, 170
Desert Sparrow Hawk, 27
Desert Thrasher, 107
Dichromatism: Two color
  shades of birds in the
  same species or brood. 4
Dickcissel, 153
Dipper, 76
Distal: unattached end of
  a part.
Distribution: natural geographic range of a spe-
  cies.
Dolichonyx, 143
  oryzivorus, 143
Domestic Hen, 35
Domestic Pigeon, 36
Dorsal: relating to the back.
Dotted Wren, 102
Doves, 36-38
Down: soft feathers, without barbules.
Downy feather, 3
Downy Woodpecker, 69
Dryobates, 61, 62, 67-69
  albolarvatus, 61
  arizonae, 62
  auduboni, 68
  borealis, 67
  cactophilus, 67
  gairdneri, 69
  gravirostris, 61
  harrisi, 68
  hyloscopus, 68
  icastus, 68
  leucothorectis, 68
  leucurus, 69
  medianus, 69
  monticola, 68
  nelsoni, 69

Figure 428

F

Figure 429

Golden-winged Warbler, 130
Gorget: conspicuous patch on throat. Fig. 431.

Figure 431

Heel: Joint at top of tarsus. Fig. 432.

Figure 432

Figure 430

Figure 433

Figure 434

L

L. Total length of a bird.
Fig. 435.

Figure 435

Figure 436

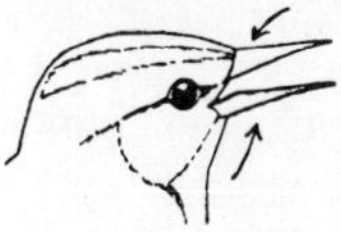

Figure 437

Figure 438

N

Figure 439

Figure 440

O

Figure 441

P

INDEX

Phalaenoptilus, 50
  californicus, 50
  hueyi, 50
  nuttalli, 50
Phasianus, 30
  colchicus, 30
  torquatus, 30
Pheasants, 30
Philadelphia Vireo, 119
Phoebe, 79, 84
Pica, 92
  hudsonia, 92
  nutalli, 92
  pica, 92
Piciformes, 60
Picoides, 63, 64
  arcticus, 63
  bacatus, 64
  dorsalis, 64
  fasciatus, 64
  tridactylus, 64
Pigeons, 36, 38
Pigeon Hawk, 27
Pigments, 3
Pileated Woodpecker, 60
Pine Grosbeak, 159
Pine Siskin, 154
Pine Warbler, 133
Pine-woods Sparrow, 175
Pinicola, 159
  alascensis, 159
  californica, 159
  enucleator, 159
  flammula, 159
  leucura, 159
  montana, 159
Pink-sided Junco, 164
Pinion: part of wing beyond the "bend". Fig. 442.

Figure 442

Pinion Jay, 90
Pipilo, 163, 166
  aberti, 166
  alleni, 163
  arcticus, 163
  bullatus, 166
  canaster, 163
  carolae, 166
  crissalis, 166
  curtatus, 163
  erthroypthalmus, 163
  falcinellus, 163
  fuscus, 166
  maculatus, 163
  megalonyx, 163
  mesoleucus, 166
  montanus, 163
  oregonus, 163
  petulans, 166
  senicula, 166
Pipits, 77
Piranga, 148, 149
  cooperi, 149
  erythromelas, 149
  flava, 149
  hepatica, 149
  ludoviciana, 148
  rubra, 149

Pitangus, 81
  derbianus, 81
  sulphuratus, 81
Plain Titmouse, 97
Plectrophenax, 169
  nivalis, 169
Ploceidae, 70
Plumage: whole feather covering of a bird.
Plumbeous: lead-colored.
Plumbeous Chickadee, 100
Plumbeous Gnatcatcher, 115
Plumbeous Vireo, 120
Plumed Quail, 34
Point Pinos Junco, 162
Polioptila, 115
  amoenissima, 115
  caerulea, 115
  californica, 115
  melanura, 115
Polyborus, 19
  auduboni, 19
  cheriway, 19
Polygamous: having more than one mate.
Pooecetes, 175
  affinis, 175
  confinis, 175
  gramineus, 175
Poor-will, 50
Post-nuptial: occuring after the breeding season.
Postorbital: back of the eye.
Prairie Chicken, 32
Prairie Falcon, 28
Prairie Marsh Wren, 105
Prairie Sharp-tailed Grouse, 32
Prairie Warbler, 133
Preacher, 119
Precocial, 6
Predacious: preying on other animals.
Pre-historic birds, 1, 2
Primary: one of the large feathers in the wing. Fig. 443.

Figure 443

Progne, 88
  hesperia, 88
  subis, 88
Prothonotaria, 128
  citrea, 128
Prothonotary Warbler, 128
Proximal: the attached end of a part.
Psaltriparus, 98
  californicus, 98
  lloydi, 98
  minimus, 98
  plumbeus, 98
Psittaciformes, 14
Ptarmigan, 30
Ptilogonatidae, 74
Puget Sound Sparrow, 171

Pupil: dark center spot in eye. Fig. 444.

Figure 444

Purple Finch, 160
Purple Grackle, 141
Purple Martin, 88
Pygmy Nuthatch, 101
Pygmy Owl, 46
Pyrocephalus, 78
  mexicanus, 78
  rubinus, 78
Pyrrhuloxia, 154
  sinuata, 154
  texana, 154

Q

Quails, 30, 34, 35
Quiscalus, 141
  aeneus, 141
  aglaeus, 141
  quiscula, 141

R

Rainier White-tailed Ptarmigan, 30
Raven, 91
Rectix: one of the principal feathers. (plural, rectrices).
Red-backed Junco, 164
Red-bellied Hawk, 24
Red-bellied Woodpecker, 66
Red-billed Pigeon, 38
Red-breasted Nuthatch, 101
Red-breasted Sapsucker, 61
Red-cockaded Woodpecker, 67
Red Crossbill, 156
Red-eyed Cowbird, 143
Red-eyed Towhee, 163
Red-eyed Vireo, 119
Red-faced Warbler, 124
Red-headed Woodpecker, 61
Red Jungle Fowl, 35
Red-naped Sapsucker, 65
Redpoll, 159
Red-shafted Flicker, 63
Red-shouldered Hawk, 24
Redstart, 123
Red-tailed Hawk, 23
Red-wing, 142
Regulus, 115
  olivaceus, 115
  satrapa, 115
Regurgitation: ejecting food from the stomach.
Resident: a bird that stays the year around in the same region.
Rhyncholophanes, 168
  mccowni, 168
Rhynchopsitta, 14
  pachyrhyncha, 14
Richardson's Grouse, 32

Figure 445

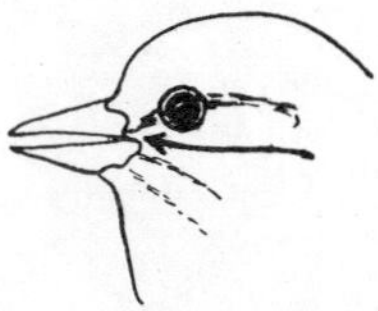

Figure 446

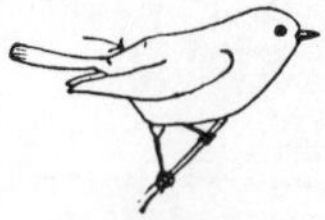

S

Figure 447

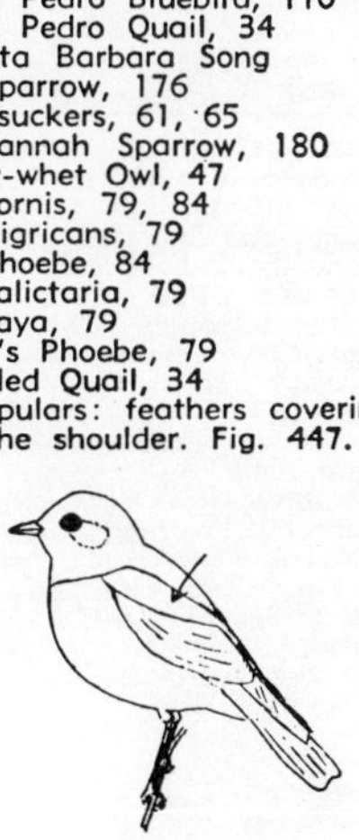

Figure 448

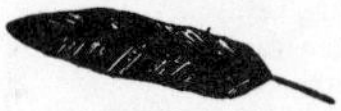

INDEX

Tail-coverts: feathers above base of tail. Fig. 449.

Figure 449

Tanagers, 148-150.
Tangavius, 143
  aeneus, 143
Tarsus: shank of bird's leg. Fig. 450.

Figure 450

Taxidermist: one who prepares and mounts animal skins.

Throat: front of neck under chin. Fig. 451.

Figure 451

Tibia: part of leg above the tarsus; the "drum stick" Fig. 452.

Figure 452

Type: typical individual, species or genus from which a group has been named.

U

Under tail-covert: feathers covering the base of the tail below. Fig. 453.

Figure 453

V

Vent: the anus.
Vernal: relating to spring.
Vertex: the crown.

Visitor: not a permanent resident.

W

W: length of wing from bend to tip. Fig. 454.

Figure 454

Web: expanded part of feather on either side.

INDEX

Figure 455

X

Y

Z

Good Night